In 2008-09 the UCL Bart[...] once again enjoyed a gr[...] named as the best UK a[...] "University Guide" and i[...] as well as in, for the sixth year running, the *Architects Journal's* annual AJ100 survey. In addition, the School has enjoyed tremendous success in the Research Assessment Exercise (RAE), placing its staff at the very forefront of international research in architectural design, history & theory, and technology.

By way of celebration, we have this year published *Bartlett Designs: Speculating with Architecture* (Wiley), which shows off the very best of student work from the last decade. Through a detailed presentation of over 100 projects, this books shows how architectural designs and ideas can creatively address some of the world's most pressing urban and social problems through buildings and other forms of architectural creativity. To all the students involved – in *Bartlett Designs*, in this year's *Catalogue* and in the Summer Show exhibition – we salute and admire you for your tremendous energy, imagination and invention.

We also acknowledge the incredible efforts and expertise of all of the Bartlett's staff, without whom none of this would be possible. We thank UCL for their continued support and investment. And we offer gratitude also to every single one of our many other contributors, sponsors and friends for their continuous and highly appreciated support.

Prof Iain Borden
Prof Christine Hawley

Head and Chair of the School
www.bartlett.ucl.ac.uk

The Bartlett School of Architecture would like to thank Allford Hall Monaghan Morris for their generous support of this year's *Catalogue*

2nd Floor, Block C
Morelands
5-23 Old Street
London EC1V 9HL
T 020 7251 5261
F 020 7251 5123
info@ahmm.co.uk
ahmm.co.uk

ne Yellow Building,
otting Dale Village

Prizes

Summer Show

The Summer Show Opener's Prize, selected by Massimiliano Fuksas and sponsored by White Partners. Awarded at the opening of the Summer Show

BSc Architecture Year 1

Herbert Batsford Prize for 'distinguished work'
Naomi Gibson

Bartlett Sessional Prize for 'good Honours standard' work
Rachel Antonio
Cherry Beaumont
Georgina Goldman

Grocers' Company Queen's Golden Jubilee Scholarship
Charlotte Baker

UCL Excellence Scholarship nomination
Naomi Gibson

BSc Architecture Year 2

Kohn Pedersen Fox Bursary for 'highest achievement of the year'
Nicholas Elias
Christopher Leung
Stefano Passeri

Maggie Scruton Memorial Travel Scholarship
Gladys Yan Yi Ching

UCL Excellence Scholarship nomination
Stefano Passeri

Fitzroy Robinson Drawing Prize for 'best drawings or models in the year'
Stefano Passeri

BSc Architecture Year 3

Grocers' Company Queen's Golden Jubilee Scholarship
Nichola Perrett

Donaldson Medal for 'distinguished work'
Tamsin Hanke

Environmental Design Prize for 'distinguished work in the integration of engineering and architectural principles in Environmental Design'
Harriet Redman

History & Theory Prize for 'distinguished work in History and Theory'
Joel Cady

Making Buildings Award
Joel Cady

Professional Studies Prize for 'distinguished work in Professional Studies'
Paul Leader-Williams

RIBA Bronze Medal nominations
Ben Hayes
Victor Hadjikyriaki

Dean's List for 'students achieving a first class degree'
Alisan Dockerty
Daniel Dodds
Tamsin Hanke
Ben Hayes
Kaowen Ho
Chiara Montgomerie
Harriet Redman
Catherine St Hill
Man FM Tang
Tim Z Yue

BSc Architectural Studies Year 3

Dean's List for 'students achieving a first class degree'
William Henderson

BSc Architecture Year Out

Henry Herbert Bartlett Travel Scholarship
Anthony Staples

Grad Dip/MArch Architecture Year 4

History & Theory Prize for 'distinguished work in History and Theory'
Dean Walker

Leverhulme Trust Bursary
Richard Hardy
Peter Webb

Owings Travel Scholarship
Janice Long Yan Lee

Rogers Stirk Harbour + Partners Bursary
Eleanor Lakin

Grad Dip/MArch Architecture Year 5

Ambrose Poynter Prize for 'distinguished work in the Diploma Thesis'
Sam McElhinney

Fitzroy Robinson Drawing Prize for 'best drawings in the year'
Katie Walmsley

Sir Banister Fletcher Medal for 'highest marks in Diploma in Architecture final examination'
Pascale Bronner

Hamiltons Prize for Design Process nominations (Winners announced at show)
James Church
Holly Lewis
Pascal Bronner
Margaret Bursa
Ric Lipson
Michiko Sumi

Leverhulme Trust Bursary
Pascale Bronner
Pernilla Ohrstedt
Luke Pearson

RIBA President's Silver Medal nominations
Pascal Bronner
Margaret Bursa

Rogers Stirk Harbour + Partners Bursary
Richard Bevan

Sir Andrew Taylor Prize for 'the best set of drawings combining construction and design'
Tetsuro Nagata

Victor Ka-Shun Chu Prize for 'excellence in design'
Joshua Scott

Commendation in Design
Kasper Ax
James Barrington
Carrie Behar
Alice Cadogan
Thomas Cartledge
Michael Hammock
Alexander Kirkwood
Holly Lewis
Yong Zheng Li
Pernilla Ohrstedt
Ital Palti
Luke Pearson
Lucas Tizard

Commendation in Thesis
Kasper Ax
Richard Bevan
Thomas Cartledge
James Church
James Davies
Michael Hammock
Lucy Jones
Yong Zheng Li
Sam McElhinney
Sze Wa Mui
Tetsuro Nagata
Nancy Ni Bhriain
Pernilla Ohrstedt
Andrew Paine
Luke Pearson
James Robertson
Declan Shaw
Matthew Shaw
James Stevens
Michiko Sumi
Timothy Tasker

Dean's List for 'students achieving a Distinction in Design'
Richard Bevan
Pascal Bronner
Margaret Bursa
Wai Lam Chan
James Church
Tom Finch
Alexander Hill
Johan Martin Hybschmann
Richard Lipson
Tetsuro Nagata
David Potts
Joshua Scott
Matthew Shaw
Michiko Sumi
George Thomson
Katie Walmsley

Professional Studies Part 3

Ross Jamieson Memorial Prize
Paz Horn
Julian Kinal

MArch Architecture

Commendation
Ruth Oldham
Johan Voordouw

Distinction
Ben Clement
Tim Norman

MArch Architectural Design

Distinction
Jana Beermann
Husain Jaorawaia
Angeliki Malakasioti
Goetz Schrader

MArch Urban Design

Commendation
Rumi Bose
Barbara E. Casini Cortesi
Xuelan Gong
Faye Antonia Hays
Miguel A. Hincapie Trivino
Aparna Joshi
Graciela Moreno
Li Na
Lavinia Rizzo-Haas

Distinction
Konstantinos Dimitrantzos
Amanda Lwin
Saurabh Vaidya

MA/MSc Architectural History

Distinction
Amber Burrow-Goldhahn
Emma Jones
Louis Moreno
Torsten Lange

Commendation
Sandra Kreidel
Gurmeet Sian

MPhil/PhD Architectural Design

AHRC Doctoral Award
Sophie Handler
Jan Kattein
Ben Sweeting
Neil Wenman

CAPES Scholarship
Ana Araujo

FCT Scholarship
Ana Luz

IKY Scholarship
Christiana Ioannou
Christos Papastergiou

Onassis Foundation Scholarship
Adam Adamis

Overseas Research Scholarship
Katherine Bash
Igor Marjanovic

*UCL Graduate School Cross Disciplinary
Research Scholarship*
Katherine Bash

MPhil/PhD Architectural History & Theory

AHRC Doctoral Award
tbc

*Canadian Social Sciences & Humanities
Research Council Scholarship*
Lea-Catherine Szacka

IKY Scholarship
Sotirios Varsamis

LKE Ozolins/RIBA Studentship
Anne Hultzsch

*Oppenheim-John Downes Memorial Trust
Award*
Alison Hand

Overseas Research Scholarship
Lea-Catherine Szacka

Royal Thai Government Scholarship
Pinai Sirikiatikul

Taiwanese Government Scholarship
Yi-Chih Huang
Shih-Yao Lai

Turkish Government Scholarship
Aslihan Senel

Contents

Exhibition Layout

The Summer Show is the annual celebration of student work at the Bartlett School of Architecture, UCL. Over 450 students show innovative drawings, models, devices, texts, animations and installations.

Exhibition opening night and party in the Main Quadrangle and the Slade Galleries of UCL, Gower St, London WC1
Fri 26 June, 6.00-10.30pm

Official show opening by Massimiliano Fuksas
Fri 26 June, 7.00pm

Exhibition open to the public
Sat 27 June, 10.00am–8.30pm
Sun 28 June, 10.00am–5.30pm
Mon 29, Tues 30 June,10.00am–6.00pm
Wed 1, Thurs 2 July, 10.00am-5.00pm
Fri 3 July, 10.00am–8.30pm
Sat 4 July, 10.00am–5.00pm (closes)

Guided exhibition tour by the Professors of the Bartlett School of Architecture, UCL
Tues 30 June, please arrive at 6.30pm for 6.45pm start, tour duration c. 1 hour

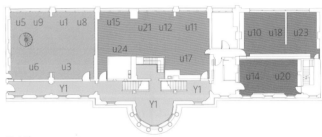

First Floor

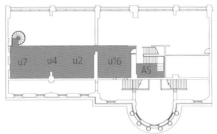

Mezzanine

BSc ArchitectureYear 1 Design

Muhammad Abd Rahman, Jae Ahn, Yll Ajvazi, Rachel Antonio, Emily Arries, Charlotte Baker, Chloe Baxter, Cherry Beaumont, Kun Bi, Ophelia Blackman, Charles Blanchard, Luke Bowler, David Caldwell, Emma Carter, Jia Chen, Jianhuang Chen, Nuozzi Chen, Ran Chen, Theclalin Cheung, Tzen Chia, Oliver Collins, Marcus Cornthwaite, Conner Cunningham, Emily Doll, Charles Dorrance King, Max Dowd, Natalia Eddy, Ivie Egonmwan, Ruthie Falkner, Frank Fan, Ying Fu, Yue Gao, Naomi Gibson, Georgina Goldman, Alicia Gonzales-Lafita, Rosemary Hahn, Ryan Hakimian, David Haslam, Mai Hitomi, Aaron Ho, Jonathan Holmes, Azuki Ichihashi, Ashleigh James, Sophia Kelleher, Anja Kempa, Rachel King, Amy Kong, Maryna Kuchak, Su Jin Kwon, Wai Lam, Samson Lau, Aaron Lee, Carmen Lee, Rebecca Li, Wendy Lin, Angela Lo, Mae Ling Lokko, Frederick Lomas, Laura Low, Titi Lucas, Sheung Tang Luk, Tess Martin, Gabrielle Masefield, Nickolas Masferton, Nabi Masutomi, Ami Matsumoto, Emily Mccaul, Samuel Mcgill, James Middelton, Ekaterina Minyaeva, Shireen Mohammadi, Gary Mok, Amada Moore, Rushda Morshed, Eri Nakagawa, Sirisan Nivatvongs, Patrick O'Callaghan, Bayan Okayeva, Augustine Ong Wing, Suet Pak, Ahmed Patel, Adam Peacock, Natalia Petkova, Rachel Pickford, Asha Pooran, Joanne Preston, Tian Qin, Muhammad Sahrum, Aimee Salata, Arub Sagib, Robert Schultes, Francesca Seal, Hongmiao Shi, Samson Simberg, Julian Siravo, Kate Slattery, Louis Sullivan, Cho-Hee Sung, Emma Swarbrick, Stanley Tan, Nada Tayeb, Jonathan Tipper, Antonia Tkachenko, William Tweddell, Fidan Uryan, Deniz Varol, Tatum Wangsatimur, Zhang Wen, Sandra Youkhana, Li Zhou

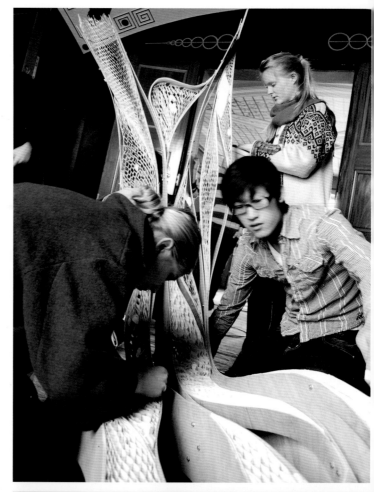

The Bartlett's BSc Architecture degree programme aims to develop a creative, diverse and rigorous approach to architecture and design from the outset. Year 1 is centred on the design studio and is taught to the year as a whole. Students observe, draw, model and design, based in the School's design studios and workshop from the first week onwards.

The main intention is to explore 'ways of seeing'; understanding and interpreting objects/events/places and learning to look beyond the visible into the unseen and 'absurd' qualities of things. In this way, a place can also be seen as something with its own identity, which each student can personally interpret. The importance of 'character' and personality is emphasised throughout the design process whether it concerns analysis, site interpretation or architectural vision. A number of recording techniques are used as a way of clarifying the subject rather than as purely graphic representation. Through being aware of the possibilities and limitations of various techniques, each student learns to express and then develop critically and appropriately, through their own intuition, an idea for an architectural proposition.

This year Sir John Soane was at the centre of all projects. Starting with a collected object the year completed his house in Ealing, Pitzhanger Manor, with a series of furniture interventions. After a mapping project in Athens each students developed an individual building proposal along a route stretching from Broadway Market and Columbia Flower Market to Brick Lane.

Year 1 Design Directors: Frosso Pimenides and Patrick Weber
Tutors: Kyle Buchanan, Lucy Leonard, Brian O'Reilly, Romed Perfler, Jonathan Pile, Juliet Quintero, Toby Smith, Nikolas Travasaros

This page and facing page: Group installations in Sir John Soanes Pitzhanger Manor House, Ealing.

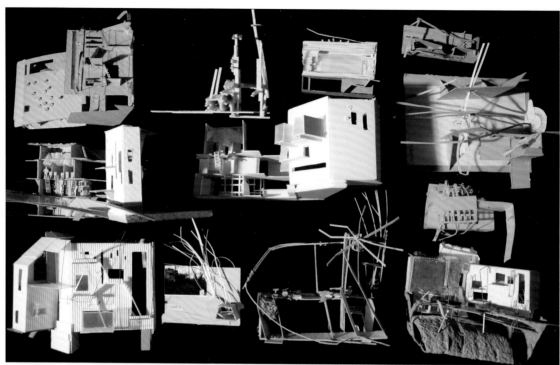

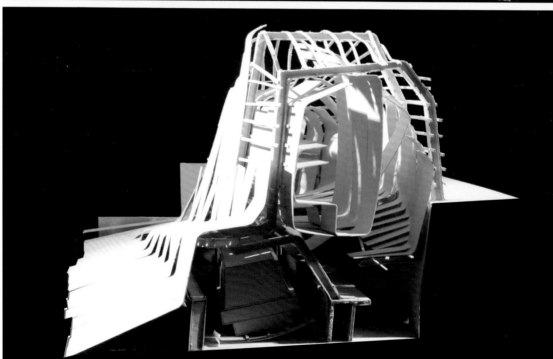

This page top Molly Yue Gao, *Bird Nest Soup Restaurant;* bottom Tess Martin, *Narrowboat Repair Workshop.*

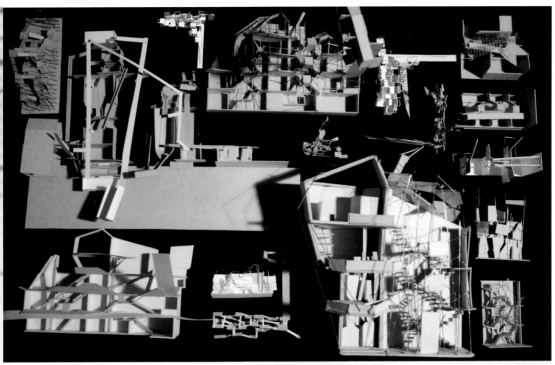

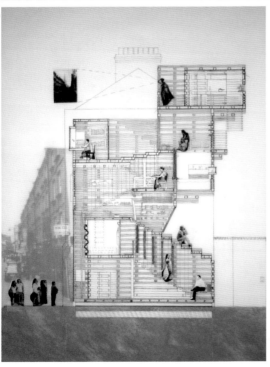

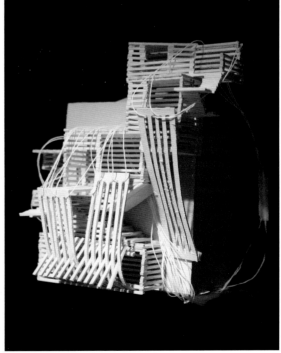

This page, top Naomi Gibson, *Experimental Brewery;* bottom Wendy Lin, *Sari Weaving Workshop.*

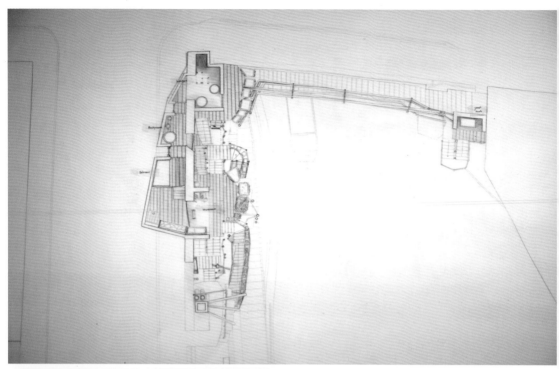

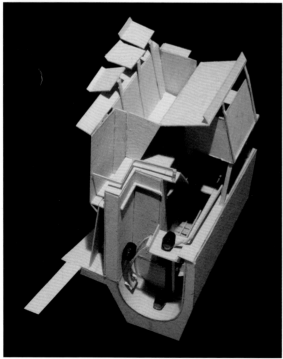

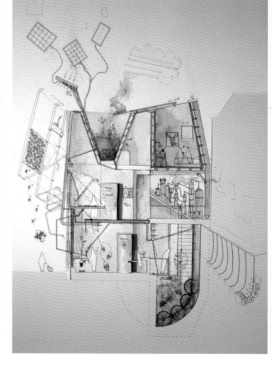

This page, top Naomi Gibson, *Experimental Brewery;* bottom Sandra Youkhana, *Flower Therapy Institute.*

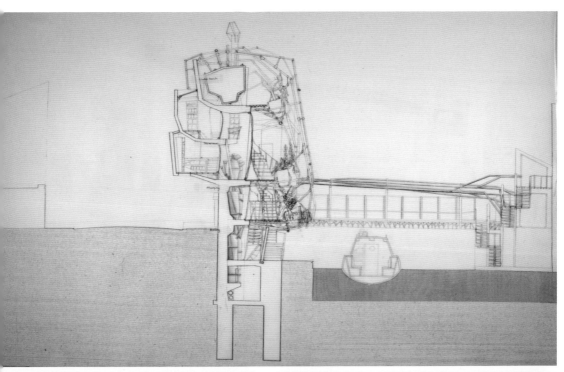

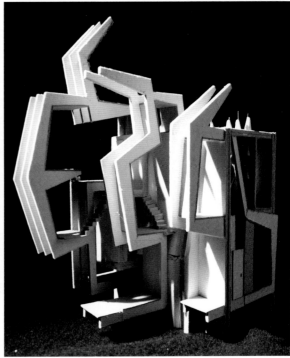

This page clockwise from the top Naomi Gibson, *Experimental Brewery*; Maryna Kuchak, *Knitting School*; Frank Fan, *Noodle Restaurant*.

BSc Unit 1

Yr 2: Yuan Gao, Rebecca Lane, Ka Man Leung, Stefanos Levidis, Thandiwe Loewenson, Kirsty Williams, Mika Zacharias Yr 3: Olivia Crawford, Alisan Dockerty, Daryl Fitzgerald, Satori Nakanishi, Rida Qureshi, Catherine St Hill, Anthony Whittaker, (Rain) Ya-Chu Wu.

Palimpsest

Resulting from scraping clean and reusing the parchment on which it is written, a palimpsest is a manuscript concealing several layers of overlapping text. Many historical works, which were considered lost, have been miraculously revealed embedded in other texts, most famously the Archimedes Palimpsest, which was discovered in Istanbul in 1907. Furthermore, the term palimpsest is used in forensic science in relation to material clues revealing the sequence of events at a crime scene, and in psychology to describe the erasing of memories in the subconscious.

Inspired by the physical and psychological metaphor of the 'palimpsest' unit one defined an architecture which is sensuous, tactile and tectonic, but also atmospheric, ephemeral, and enigmatic.

We studied layered spaces, composed of multiple overlaid 'scripts' forming a meaning greater than the sum of their component parts; haunted spaces, when a distinctive contrasting atmosphere trails the physical materiality of a place; repressed spaces, purposefully concealed or veiled in habit; weathered spaces, where the patina of time creates an accrued effect of erasure and enigmatic spaces, where missing links produce diverse interpretations.

And we asked, how can we design buildings that exist in time? Can a reading of sites with deep-reaching history inspire designs that resonate far into the future?

The focus of our investigation was Istanbul, the city as palimpsest, constructed as a thick tapestry of interwoven layers.

Penelope Haralambidou and Michael Tite

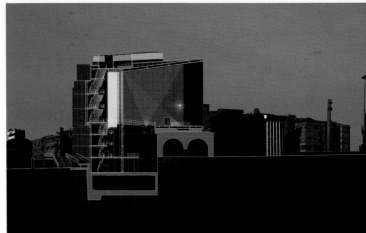

Clockwise from top left: Thandi Loewenson, *Local Newspaper and Printing Press, Tarlabasi*; Satori Nakanishi, *Kurdish Pirate Radio Station*; Yuan Gao, *Feed the Horse, Children's Game*; Satori Nakanishi, *TRT TV Station, Taksim Square*; Rebecca Lane, *Turkish Folk Music Machine*; Olivia Crawford, *Spa and Turkish Bath, Aldgate*.

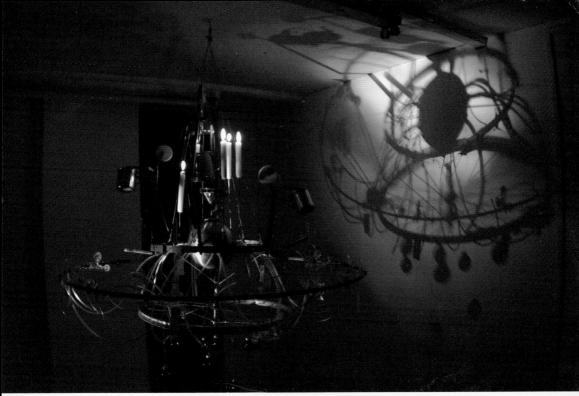

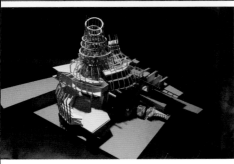

Clockwise from top left: Ka Man Leung, *Magic Mirror Chandelier;* Mika Zacharias, *AubergineMachine;* Kirsty Williams, *Seismology Research Station and Library, Balat;* Ka Man Leung, *Pigeon Post Office, Balat;* Kirsty Williams, *Hagia Sophia Suitcase.*

Clockwise from top left: Anthony Whittaker, *Istanbul Film Institute;* Ka Man Leung, *Pigeon Post Office, Balat;* Daryl Fitzgerald, *Fishmongers and Restaurant, Kings Cross;* Olivia Crawford, *Swimming Pool, Ortakoy;* Mika Zacharias, *Turkish Cookery School, Karakoy.*

Opposite top: Alisan Dockerty, *Mackerel Smoke House, Shoreditch.* Bottom: Alisan Dockerty, *Water Ecology Institute, Bigli University.*

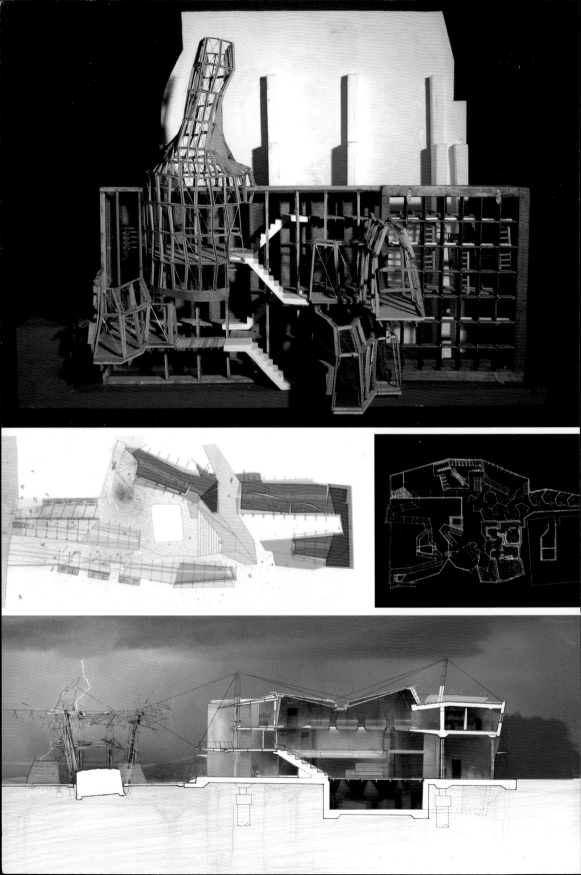

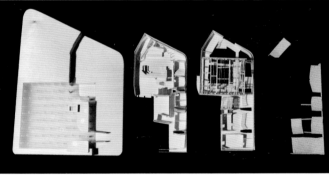

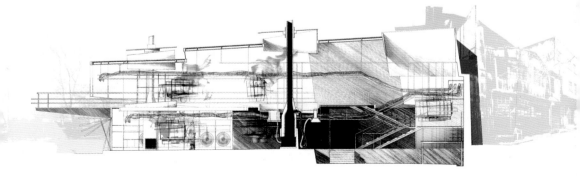

Opposite clockwise from top left: Cate St.Hill, *Writers' Hotel, Bloomsbury;* Rida Qureshi *Electronic Music School, Kuzguncuk;* Daryl Fitzgerald *Sinking Theatre, Karakoy;* Stefanos Levidis, *Sinop Boatyard and Cafe, Karakoy.*
This page clockwise from top left: Cate St.Hill, *Library for Turkish Literature;* Rain Wu, *Women's Community Centre and Domestic Violence Clinic, Balat;* Mika Zacharias, *Turkish Cookery School, Karakoy;* Rain Wu, *Birthing Centre, Maida Vale.*

BSc Unit 2

Yr 2: Will Armstrong, Jason Claxton, Hugh
Scott Moncrieff, Risa Nagasaki, Joe Paxton
Camille Thuillier, John Wu, Emily Yan.
Yr 3: Mark Attmore, Diego Cano Lasso, Keti
Carapuli, Daniel Dodds, James Blaze Burn
Sale, Claire Taggart, Ahmad Zahrif.

Urban Sting

A sting is a small delicate action which
can cause a great effect. What happens
when something is transported from one
culture to another, and begins to change
the surrounding environment? What
happens architecturally, when a new
element is placed into an existing space,
and changes activities on a much larger
scale? We are concerned with creating
architecture which is dynamic, never quite
the same today as tomorrow, fading
away, reappearing unexpectedly, altering
with the light. This means looking not
just at the design of the object, but also
considering its effects on the surrounding
society, the way its influence begins to
spread.

The year began with a weekend visit to
Lubeck, an island city in North Germany,
its internal structure defined by five large
and magnificent mediaeval churches. The
students used one of the churches for the
construction of a temporary installation
and as a site for a small building project,
inserting an unexpected function into the
ex-isting fabric. We examined the City
of London, a strange mix of large-scale
financial institutions placed into the street
pattern of historic London.Unpredicted
new activities were proposed to create a
set of individual architectural proposals.

Thanks to our guest critics: Stephen
Gage, Christine Hawley, Laura Allen,
Ben Stringer, Johannes M-Lotze, Guvenc
Topcuoglu, Ricardo Ostos, Simon Herron,
Susanna Isa, Luke Olson, Max Kahlen, Ben
Addy, Rashid Ali and Matthew Butcher.

Julian Krueger, Julia Backhaus,
William Firebrace

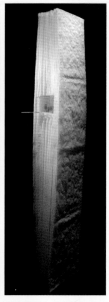

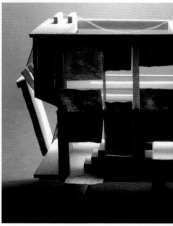

Clockwise from top left: Claire Taggart, *City Model Box;* Various Students *Marrakech Books;*
Diego Cano Lasso, *Structural paper dress;* Camille Thuillier, *Archery club, building insertion
for the Aegidien church;* Risa Nagasaki, *Papersting;* Emily Yan, *Acrobats theatre in the
Marienkirche;* Lubeck; James Sale, *Papersting.*

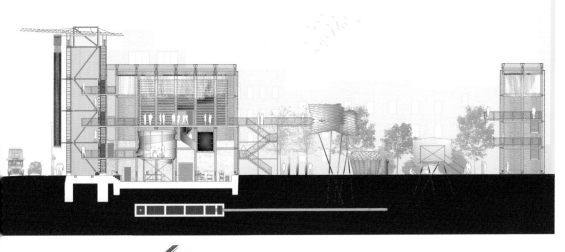

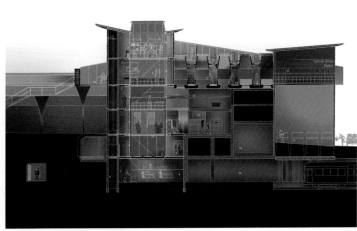

Top: James Blaze, *Burn Sale: Building for the London Paper Guild, Bishopsgate, Large parts of the building are made out of paper. The building provides an assembly hall, a paper workshop and an archive;* Middle: John Wu, *Dyeing Workshop and shop for fashion accessories Cannon Street Station;* Bottom left: Joe Paxton, *Floating Teahouse, River Thames;* Bottom right: Hugh Scott Moncrieff, *Herbal garden and apothecary, Cannon Street Station.*

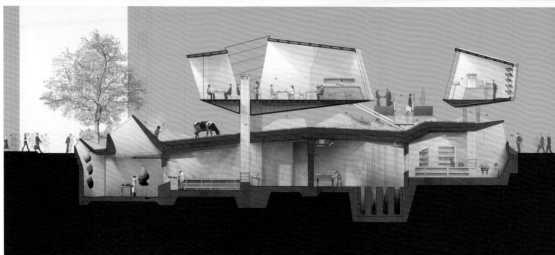

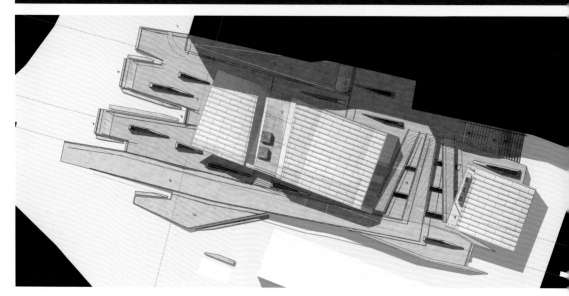

Top: Mark Attmore, *The London City Barn introduces a piece of rural Britain to the city. It provides flexible office spaces for redundant city workers, a food market and a restaurant for traditional British food.* Middle: Daniel Dodds, *The Nose to Tail Complex aims at reintroducing the direct relationship between the manufacturing process and the consumers to the city. Restaurant and leather workshop/ meat and leather production.* Bottom: Daniel Dodds, *Nose to Tail Complex, Roof plan.*

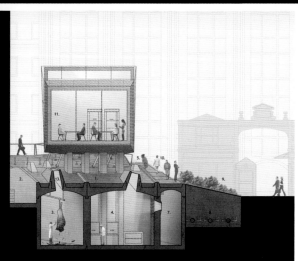

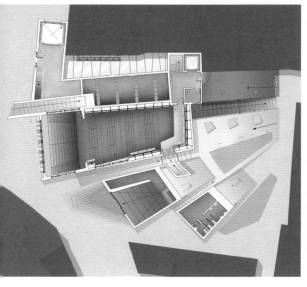
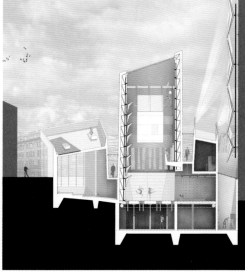

Top left: Mark Attmore, *The London City Barn. Section model.* Top right: Keti Carapuli, *Model study.* Middle left: Daniel Dodds, *The Nose to Tail Complex, Short section.* Middle right: Daniel Dodds, *London City model box.* Bottom: Claire Taggart: *Theatre and performing landscape. The theatre can open up and activate parts of the surrounding area as performance space.*

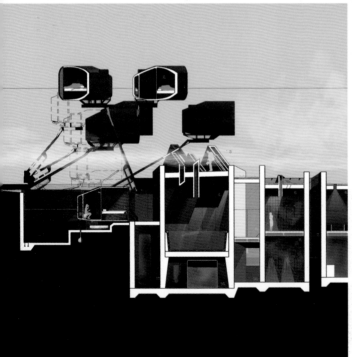

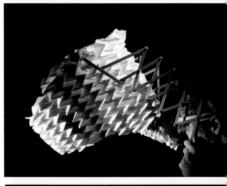

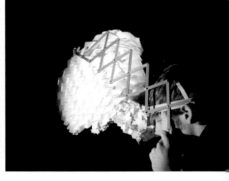

Top: Claire Taggart, *Theatre and performing landscape, Section model.* Bottom right: Will Armstrong, *Hamam and capsule hotel in the City of London, short section.* Bottom left: Will Armstrong, *Papersting, defragmenting persicope.* Right page: Will Armstrong, *Hamam and capsule hotel.* Top: *Perspective view.* Bottom: *Roof plan, Groundfloor plan.*

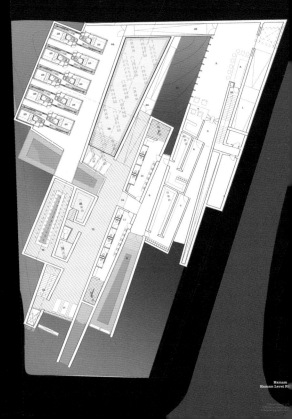

Hamam
Hamam Level Pl

BSc Unit 3

Yr 2: Maria Goustas, Peivand Mirzaei, Hyder Mohsin, Sabina Nobi, Stefano Passeri, Francesca Pringle, Rupert Rampton, Jaymar Vitangcol, Imogen Webb. Yr 3: Leander Adrian, Gabriel Chung, Katie Fudge, Sonila Kadillari, Joyce Lau, Meng Lui, Yan Yan.

Embedded Ecologies

A host can generally be described as providing some kind of benefit to whatever organism inhabits it. Sometimes this relationship is parasitic and other times it is mutually beneficial. There are obviously a multitude of examples in nature and there are a wide cross section of nuances and differences in how this balance of benefit exists. Unit 3 sought to investigate the roles of hosts and symbiotes and as a corollary developed synthetic ecologies which explore such multi-layered and interactive relationships. The control and exchange of energies that are implied in such a relationship formed a strategy for an architecture and tactic for urban interventions. Students were given two discrete tasks for the year.

In the first, students were asked to find a host. Critically this is an environment, place or object that has very particular and identifiable characteristics. This site is not a blank canvas and it is not inert. Students considered a choice of host that had a very particular set of requirements or needs; it placed particular demands on its inhabitants that made a significant contributions to the projects. An architecture of symbiosis between host and occupying agent developed.

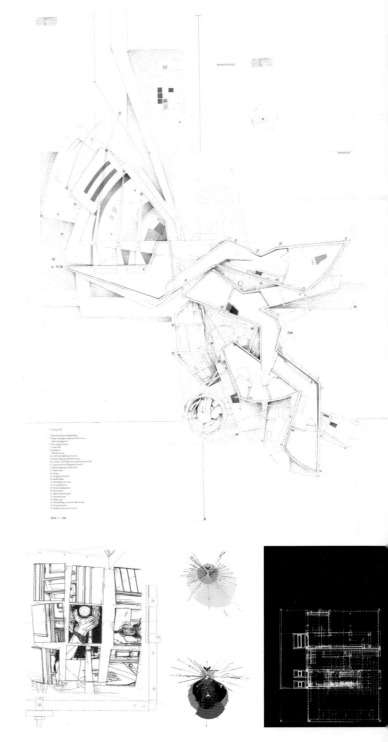

Abigail Ashton and Andrew Porter

Top: Sonila Kadillari, *Harlem Music School and Playground*. Bottom left to right: Rupert Rampton, *Fractured Vision*; Jaymar Vitangcol, *Manhattan Pigeon Loft*; Maria Goustas, *Tribeca Cinema*.

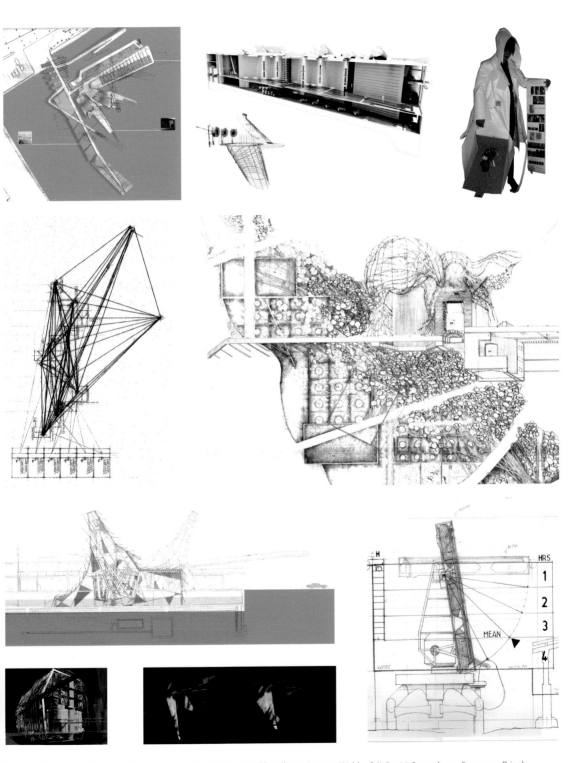

Top row: Hyder Mohsin, *Oyster Allotments*; Leander Adrian, *Brooklyn Library*; Imogen Webb, *Crit Coat 1*. Second row: Francesca Pringle, *Inverse Proportional Weave*; Meng Liu, *Grandma's House*. Bottom row (clockwise from top left): Joyce Lau, *Manhattan Oyster Farm*; Stefano Passeri, *Greenwich Tidal Mirror*; Sabina Nobi, *Paper Balloons*; Yan Yan, *Manhattan Fashion School*.

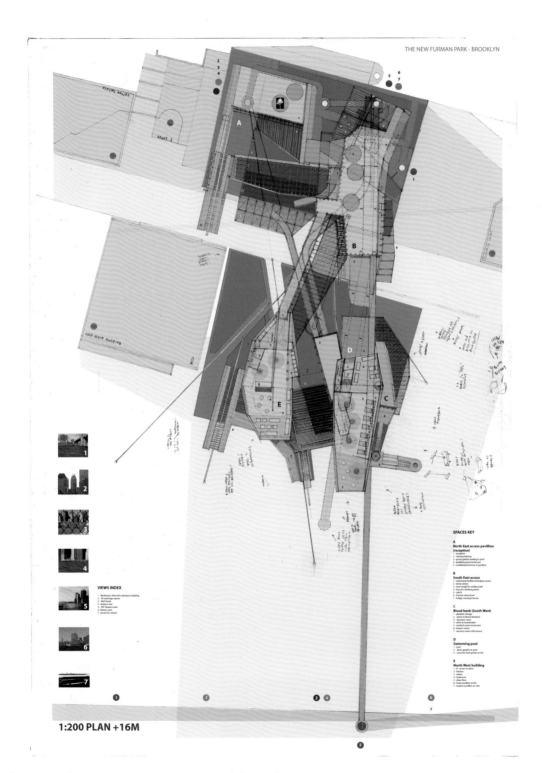

THE NEW FURMAN PARK - BROOKLYN

VIEWS INDEX

1. Manhattan skyline & entrance building
2. 30 exchange square
3. Wall Street
4. Hudson river
5. NYC blood center
6. Battery park
7. Governors Island

SPACES KEY

A
North East access pavillion (reception)
1. reception
2. viewing balcony
3. paved garden leading to pool
4. paddling pool (sunfloor)
5. cantilevered former-it pavillion

B
South East access
1. swimming facilities/changing rooms
2. decks stream
3. rear trough for rooftop park
4. steps for climbing plants
5. cafe E
6. Furman street level
7. bridge crossing Furman

C
Blood bank (South West)
1. plasmatic storage
2. hatch to blood donation
3. donation room
4. reception & examination
5. medical waste incinerator
6. freezer rooms
7. recovery room with tissues

D
Swimming pool
1. pool
2. decks garden to pool
3. concrete hard garden at rim

E
North West building
1. lift - access to diner
2. kitchen
3. toilets
4. cloakroom
5. diner floor
6. lower pavillion at the
7. Hudson pavillion at rim

1:200 PLAN +16M

Stefano Passeri, *The New Furman Street Park and Blood Bank (Brooklyn)*.

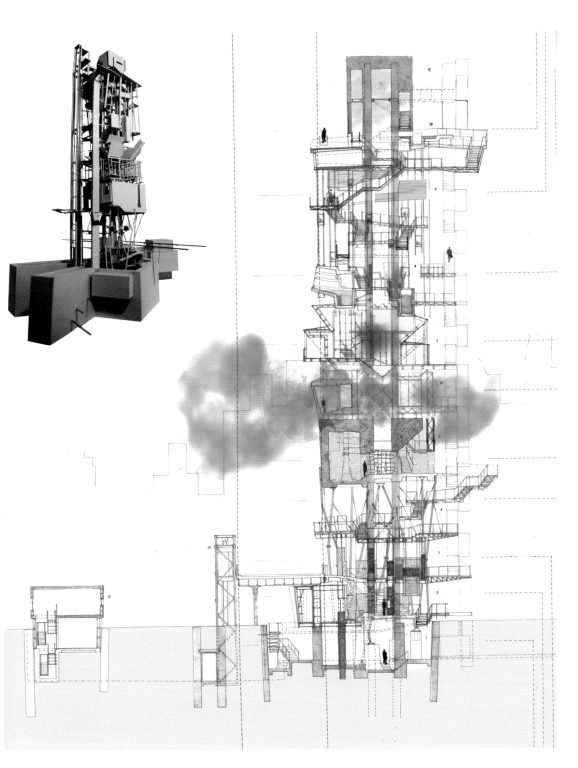

Gabriel Chung, *Landfill Tower Manhattan*.

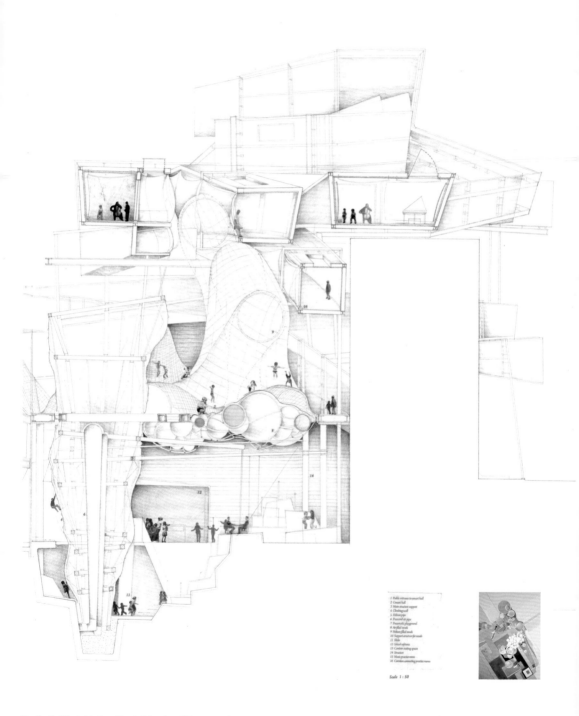

Sonila Kadillari, *Harlem Music School and Playground.*

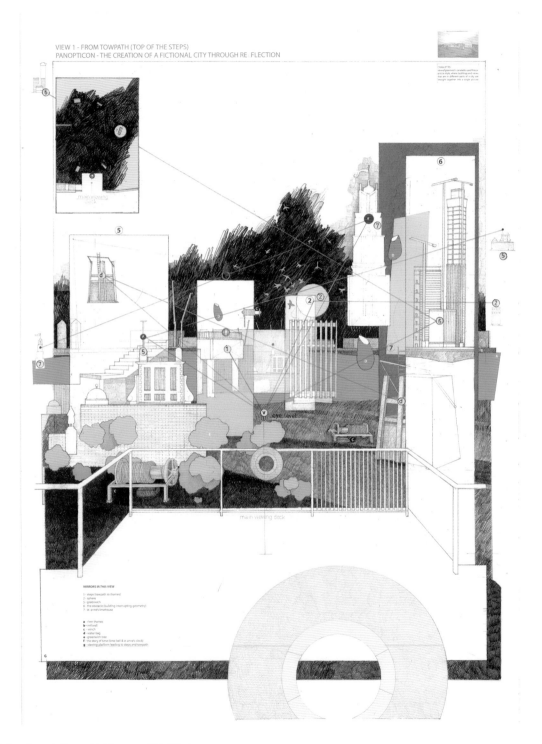

Stefano Passeri, *Greenwich Mirrors and Tidal Clock*.

BSc Unit 4

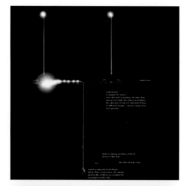

Yr 2: Karen Au, Robert Burrows, Anton Chernikov, Haesung Choi, Eleonora Hadjigeorgiou, Grace Mark, Lucy Rothwell. Yr 3: Jonathan DeWind, Yong Lik Lee, Young Woo Lee, Nicola Perrett, Marcos Polydorou, Felicity Price-Smith, Harriet Redman, Suyang Xu.

Nothing is Neutral

This year our architectural proposals inhabit, interface and amplify selected elements from the mesh of natural forces, urban patterns and sociopolitical contexts which form a liquid web of material in the Docklands, East London. We have evolved increasingly complex relationships between our multiple proposals and the urban context, establishing a network of inextricable links creating an environmental metamorphosis. Our investigations acknowledge and celebrate cultural differences, histories, narratives and memories, anticipating how the future of what we propose is fused with the footprint of history. They aim to facilitate an alternative to the blanket regeneration sweeping through East London.

U4 would like to thank: Laura Allen, Jan Birksted, Iain Borden, Jolyon Brewis, Marcos Cruz, Lorna Davies, Michael Faulkner, Bernd Felsinger, Stephen Gage, Elliott Hodges, Gerry Judah, James Khamsi, Saskia Lewis, cj Lim, Mark Middleton, Deborah Miller, Robin Monotti, Erik Orts-Hansen, Stuart Piercy, Mike Reynolds with 'Earthship Biotecture', Justin Sayer, Mark Smout and Rosie Winston.

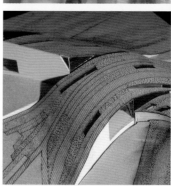

Mark Ruthven and Jerry Tate

Clockwise from top left: Suyang Xu, Lucy Rothwell, Felicity Price-Smith, Eleonora Hadjigeorgiou, Lucy Rothwell, Robert Burrows, Nicola Perrett

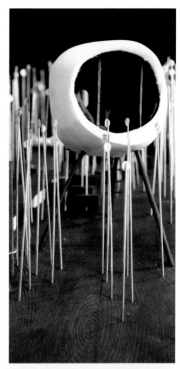

Top left: Marcos Polydorou. Top right and bottom: Harriet Redman

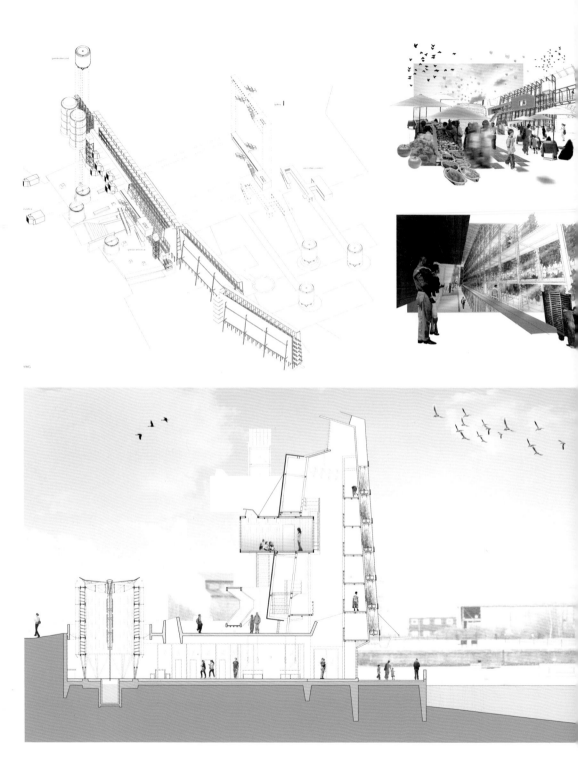

This page: Yong Lik Lee, *Silvertown Tomato City*.

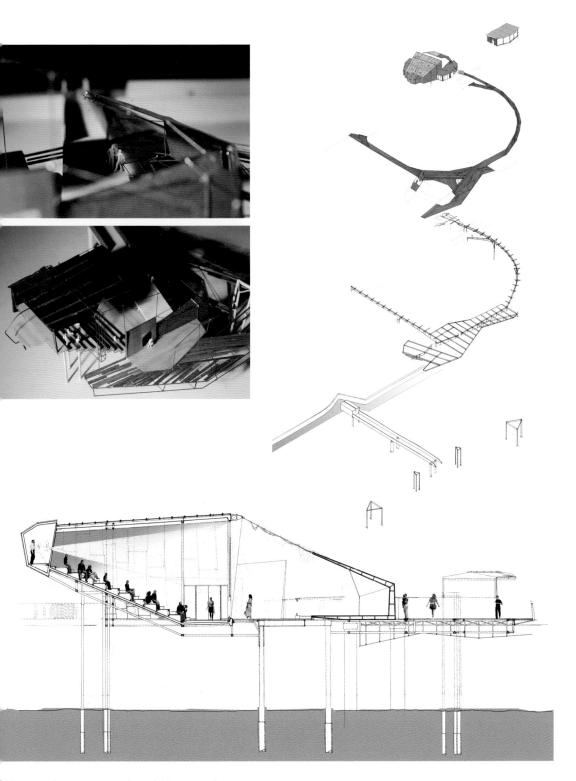

This page: Robert Burrows, *North Woolwich Promenade.*

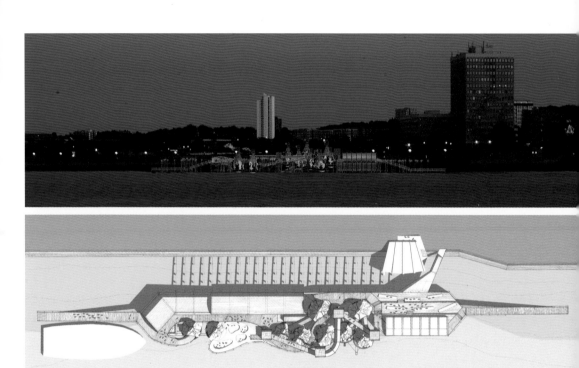

This and facing page: Harriet Redman, *South Woolwich Pleasure Pier*.

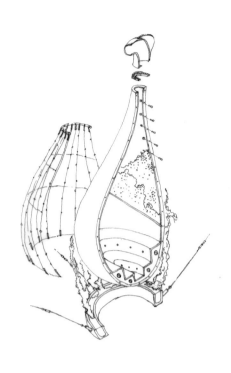

BSc Unit 5

Yr 2: Vinicius Machado Cipriano, Joseph Dejardin, Amelia Hunter, Megan Townsend, Max Walmsley, Yuchen Wang.
Yr 3: Janinder Bhatti, Victor Hadjikyriacou, Tamsin Hanke, Hong Jin Leow, Dhiren Patel, Chi Ian Philip Poon, Martin FM Tang.

Nothing is Neutral

pi·o·neer

1. First person to explore territory: a person who is one of the first from another country or region to explore or settle a new area

2. Inventor or innovator: a person or group that is the first to do something or that leads in developing something new

Within many cultures there has often been the desire to pioneer and travel to unknown territory in search for a new beginning. It was the pioneer trails and settlements that discovered unexplored worlds and distinguished the known from the unknown. Pioneering was associated with risk taking, determination and persistence but most of all curiosity. The French philosopher Michel Foucault states that 'curiosity' evokes an acute interest in and concern for everything that exists, a sharpened sense of reality, a readiness to find what surrounds us strange and odd; a certain determination to throw off familiar ways of thought and to look at the same things in a new and different way; a passion for seizing what is happening now and what is disappearing; a lack of respect for the traditional hierarchies of what is important and fundamental. This year the unit went on a journey to venture out to hidden territories, new realities, strange and overlooked spaces. We investigated landscapes that inhabit the ambiguous zone between human and natural environment and wonder about the existence of yet undiscovered universes.

In true pioneer spirit, we took risks and speculated about inventive, experimental and innovative architectural propositions.

**Julia Backhaus and
Pedro Font Alba**

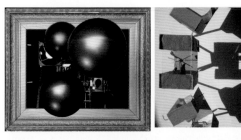

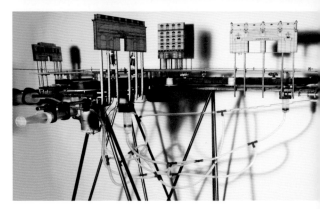

Clockwise from top left. Martin Tang, *Pioneering Weather;* Joseph Desjardin, *Hook's Portrait;* Megan Townsend, *The Warren;* Max Walmsley, *No-Mansland;* Yuchen Wang.

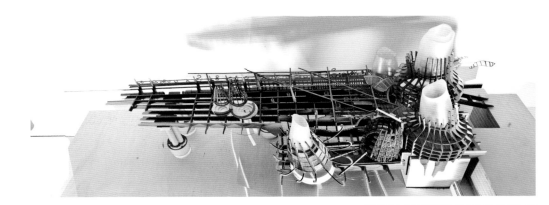

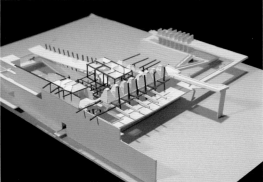

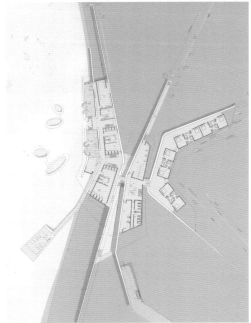

Clockwise from top left. Martin Tang, *Pioneering Weather;* Vinicius Cipriano, *Homage to Donald Judd;* Janinder Bhatti, *Salt Spa;* Amalia Hunter, *Hollywood horses;* Janindfer Bhatti, *Moss Garden.*

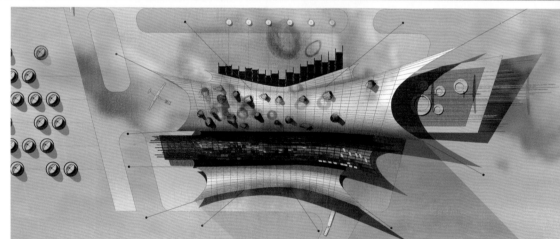

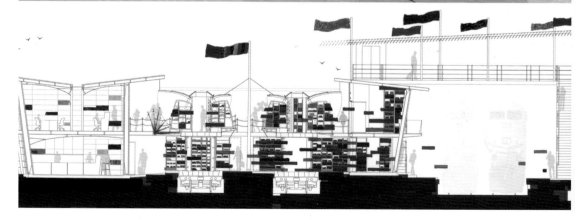

Top and middle: Martin Tang; *Gliders Club – The Wind Puppet*. Bottom: Jin Hong Leow, *Mobile Market in Marfa*.

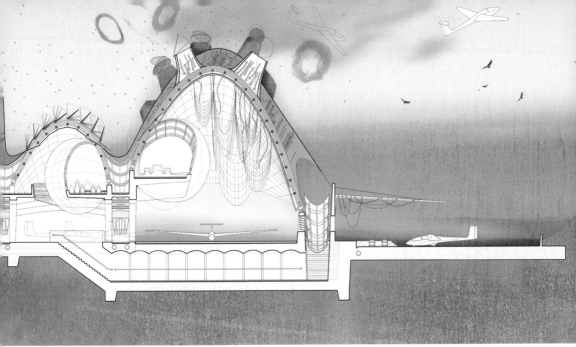

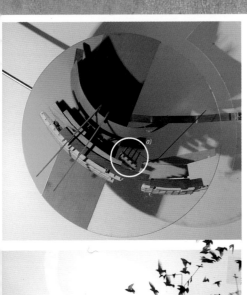

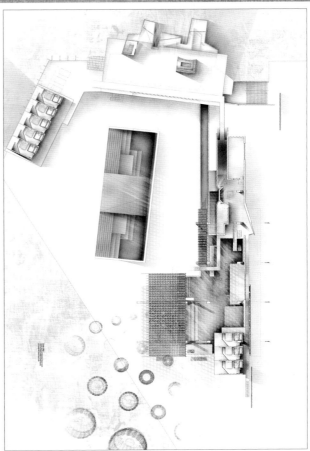

Above left: Philip Poon; *Bird's Pavillion in Regents Park*. Above Right: Philip Poon, *Marfa Lights*.

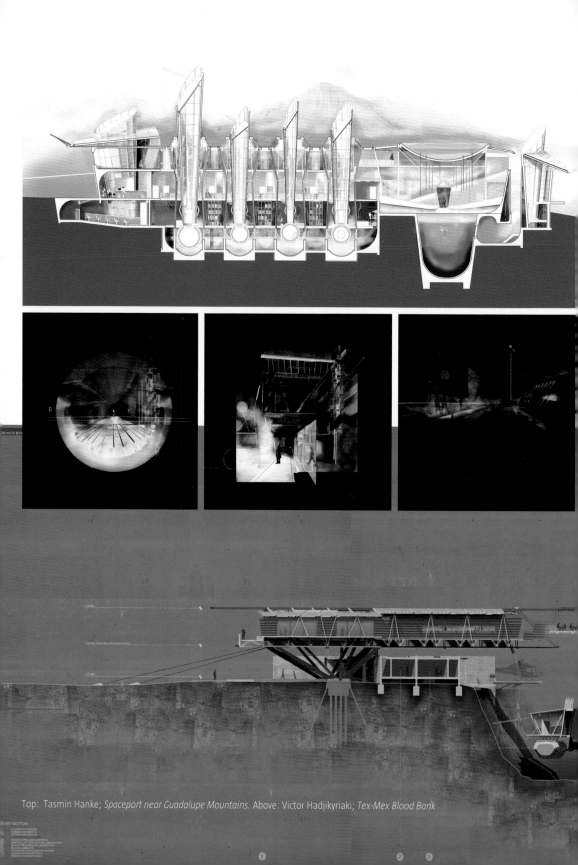

Top: Tasmin Hanke; *Spaceport near Guadalupe Mountains*. Above: Victor Hadjikyriaki; *Tex-Mex Blood Bank*

This page:. Victor Hadjikyriaki; *Tex-Mex Blood Bank*

BSc Unit 6

Yr 2: Nicholas Blomstrand, Rebecca Thompson, Matteo Imran Perretta, Joe Gautrey, Nicholas Elias, David Rhys Jones, Chris Mobbs. Yr 3: Aisyah Nur MD Ajib, Aminah Babikir, Alistair Shaw, Joel Cady, Imogen Holden, Jake Attwood-Harris, Michelle Young

Altered States

"Going mad is the only way of staying sane." - J.G.Ballard

Lost on strange islands suspended within the familiar spaces of the everyday is the vagabond troupe of DIY eccentrics, adventurers and malcontents who conjure their own atlas of Micronations. These fictional states vary in physical scale from the islands of 17th century pirate utopias, to an abandoned anti aircraft tower in the middle of the North Sea or the sitting room of an anonymous flat in east London. They merge fact, myth and speculation in their embrace of a parallel world, motivated by political subterfuge, legal loopholes, an immoderate love of royal titles, or a disenchantment with the commonplace.

This year Unit 6 authored our own archipelago of fictional states. We navigated this critical space between the actual and the imagined, a space where architecture can enter into new relations with the territories of science and fiction. We wandered off the map, through the speculative landscapes of dreams and desires, on a future safari into brave new worlds that have mutated from our own. These projective states are actually readings of the world we are now in, an experience of the present as a site of possible futures. Projects slip suggestively between mistakes, myths and lies – a 'combinatory capacity' of infinite and unsettling possibilities.

Paolo Zaide and Liam Young

Top: Rebecca Thompson, *Nightmare Glasses.* Middle: Chris Mobbs, *Underground myth recreation.* Bottom: Alistair Shaw, *Open source Fashion Taste initiative.*

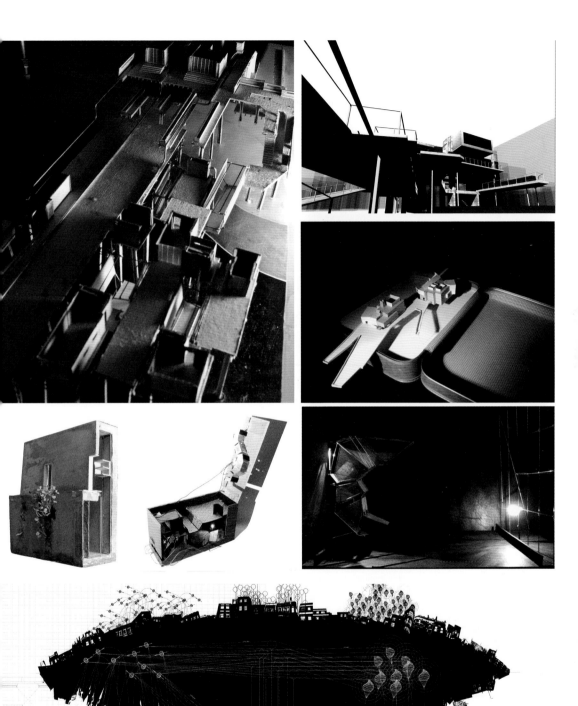

Top left: Michelle Young, *Border Control*. Right (top to bottom): Nicholas Blomstrand, David Rhys Jones, Jake Attwood-Harris. Middle left: Joel Cady, Jake Attwood-Harris, *Route of interior illusions*. Bottom: Imran Perretta, *An archaeology of Brick Lane*.

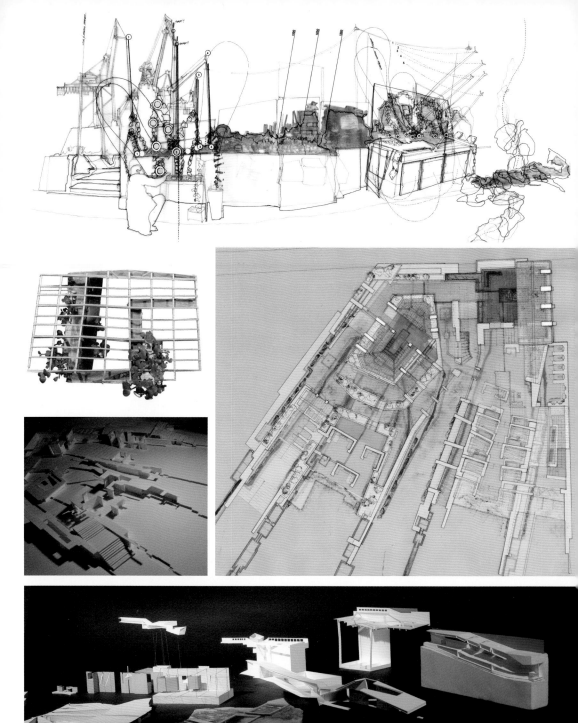

Clockwise from top-left: Nicholas Elias, *Istanbul mapping; market place;* Imogen Holden, *Charcoal water gardens;* Joel Cady, *The Olympic Dreamer's Models;* Imogen Holden; Joel Cady.

s page: Imran Perretta. Allotments for retired Hooligans

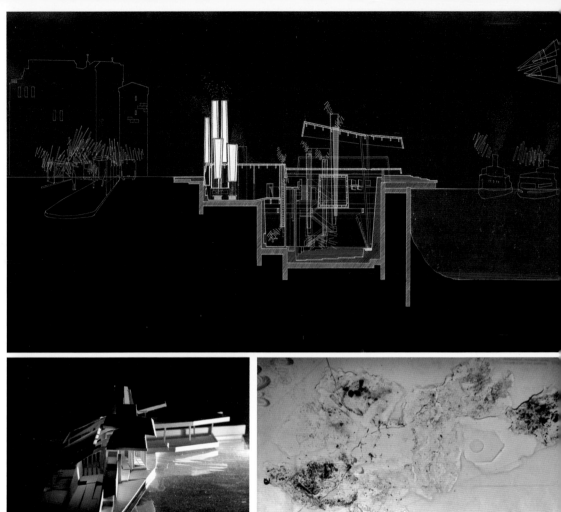
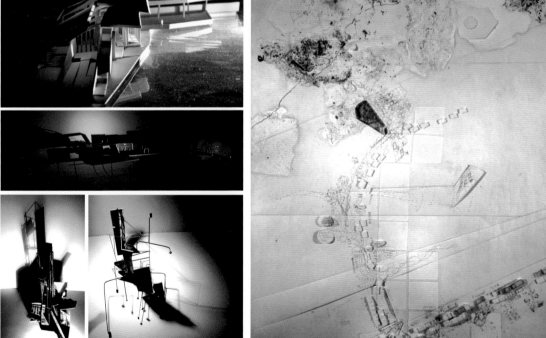

Clockwise from top: Aisha Nur MD Ajib, *Subterranean refuge of sounds and smells;* Aisha Nur MD Ajib, *Sensory Borders;* Aminah Babikir, *7 London Gates [two shown];* Joe Gautrey, Chris Mobbs, *Secular Celebration.*

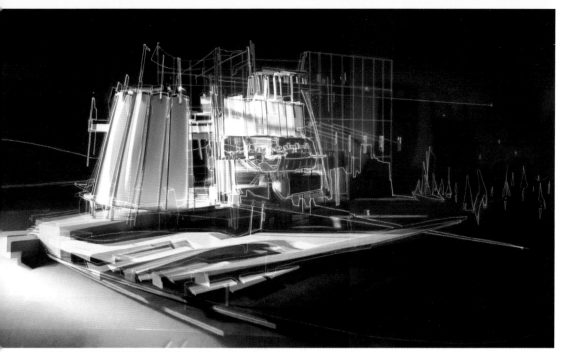

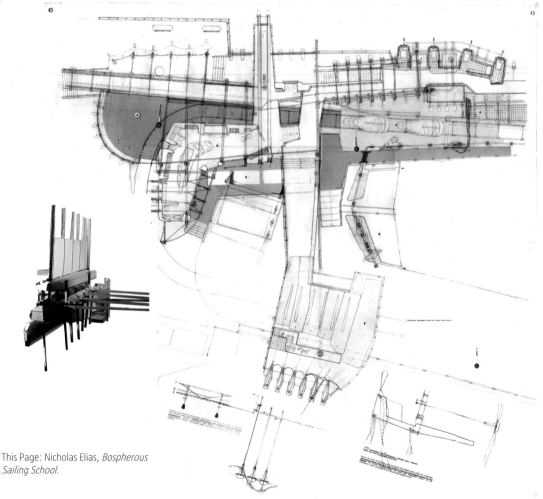

This Page: Nicholas Elias, *Bospherous Sailing School*.

BSc Unit 7

Yr 2: Gladys Ching, Frances Heslop, Stanley Ho, Bethan Knights, Simone Persadie, Isabelle Priest, Joshua Stevenson-Green.
Yr 3: Jane Brodie, Yu-Wei Chang, Banksie Critchley, Tom Kendall, Dos Nilkhamhaeng, Lucy Ottewell, Dimple Rana, Eryk Ulanowski

The Empire of Architecture: Obsession and Obstruction

Empires are not formed by whimsical desire, nor are they easily achieved - they are driven by obsession bearing adversity over obstruction. Unlike political empires whose states governed through military command and political coercion, the Empire of Architecture governs by aesthetic or literary coercion. Be it the British empire (political) which stretched to the far East, or the Modernist empire (architecture) which has global repercussions to this day, both forms of empire have shown their common desires and can proliferate beyond the cultural and ethnic centres of their origin.

What makes an Empire of Architecture distinct from the multitude of prolific aesthetic styles is the rigorous resolution at every level: from the masterplan, through the philosophy, the execution of drawings to the final details - an architectural empire speaks of a wider growth; an extension of ideas beyond the boundaries of the site that can spread its language globally and with longevity over time. To this day the Modernist empire governs many an architectural practice, even if its foundations are somewhat forgotten...

This year in Unit 7, we encouraged students to discover the beginnings of their empire; embracing their obsessions to overcome the obstructions of their challenge.

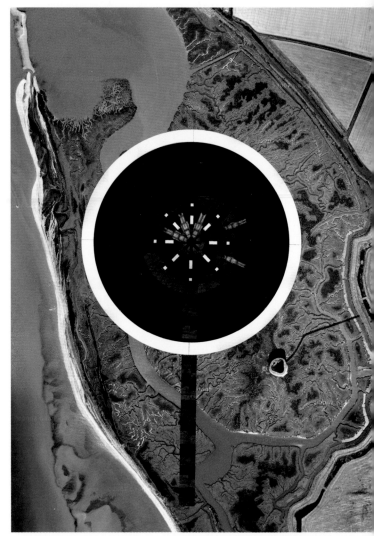

Dan Brady and Jan Kattein

Above: Eryck Ulanowski.

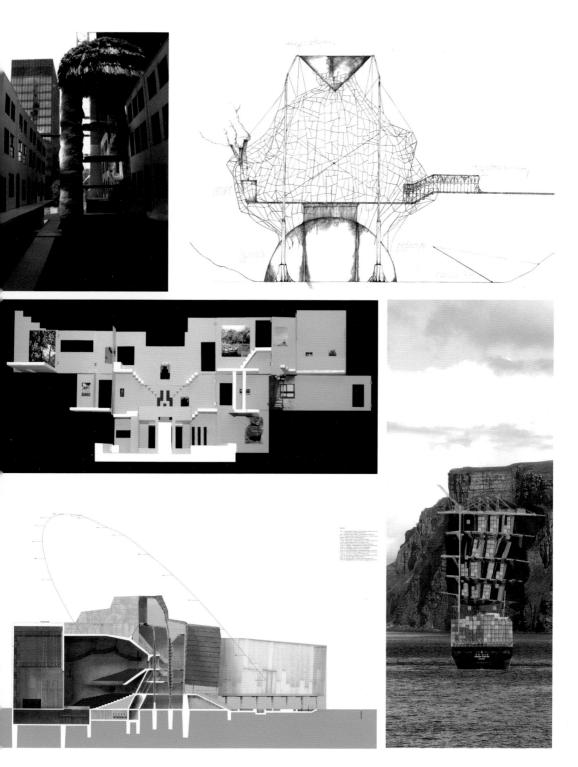

Clockwise from top left: Isabelle Priest, Joshua Green-Stevenson, Lucy Ottewell, Eryck Ulanowski, Yu-Wei Chang.

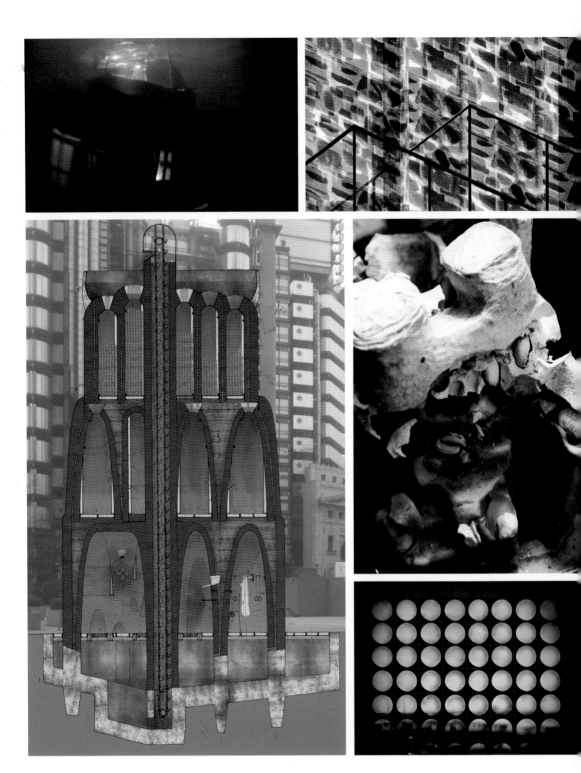

Clockwise from top left: Jane Brodie, Gladys Ching, Stanley Ho, Frances Heslop, Banksie Critchley.

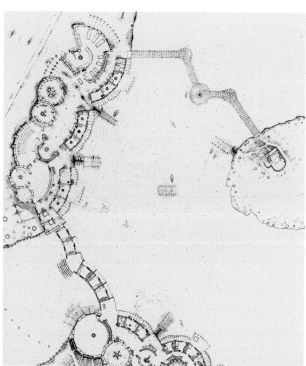

Clockwise from top left: Stanley Ho, Dimple Rana, Bethan Knights.

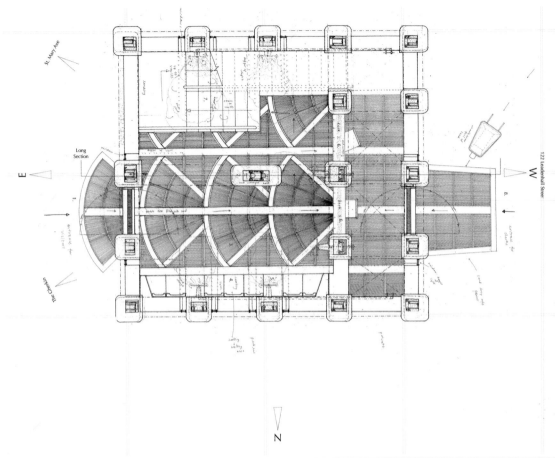

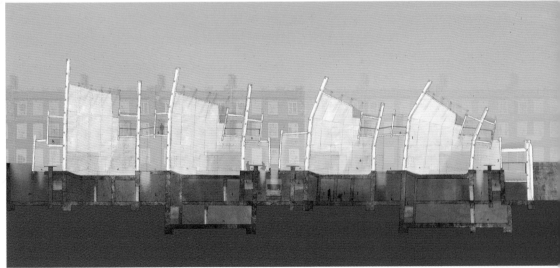

This page: Banksie Critchley

This page: Tom Kendall

BSc Unit 8

Yr 2: Keiichi Iwamoto, Daniel James Lane, Michael Christopher Pugh, Yuan Zhao, Alexander Zhukov. Yr 3: Emi Bryan, XueTing Cai, Theodore Games Petrohilos, Ben Hayes, Kaowen Ho, Ejiri Kenzo, Chiara Montgomerie, Olivia Pearson, Francis Roper, Yong Jun Song.

Good Night Past, Good Morning Future

Good Night Past, Good Morning Future Scaled scenarios for cities of the future have forever been an indulgence of architects. The modern age has seen frequent utopian proposals, with Le Corbusier, Fuller and Frank Lloyd Wright being key names in advocating change. Technological advancements have now made some of these futures reality, while other discarded ideas have found a second life in museums and archives - cultural repositories for aspirations of the past, present and future.

As far as built environments go, New York still stands as one of the ultimate examples of the advances of urban, technological and cultural thought, a realised utopia. We will take an interest in the histories that shaped our image of New York as a 'city of the future'. Through these stories we will look at the city's current state of evolution and propose imaginative, unexpected, perhaps strange, but compelling avenues for the city to follow. How can we glance a vision of the future in a city that has already seen it...?

Johan Berglund and Rhys Cannon

Clockwise from top left: Ben Hayes, *The Harlem Experiment*; Daniel Lane, *Newspaper Archive*; Emi Bryan, *School of Illusion*; Keiichi Iwamoto, *1:100 Colonisation Vessel*; Francis Roper, *Immigration Support Facility*.

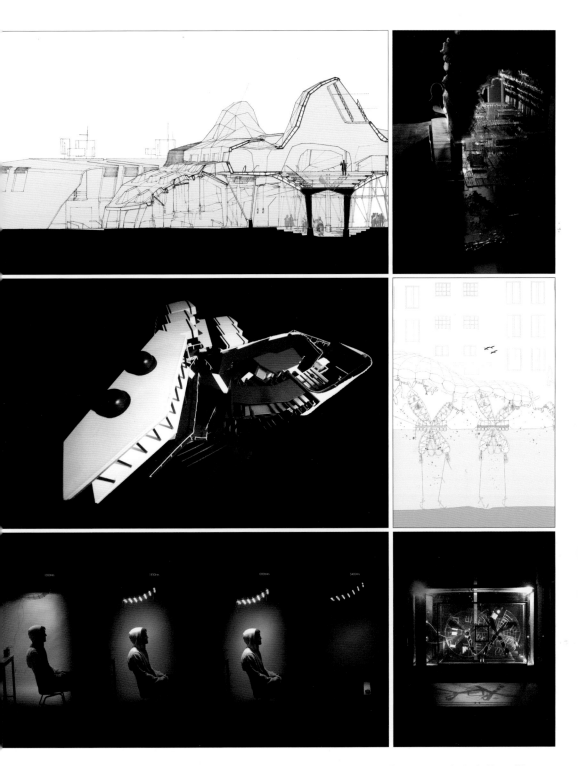

Clockwise from top left: Theo Games Petrohilos, *Williamsburg Town Hall*; Olivia Pearson, *Museum of Dust*; Snow Cai, *Dissolvable Pavillion*; Jun Song, *Box of Memories*; Francis Roper, *Body/Light Interface*; Kenzo Ejiri, *Firemen's Retreat*.

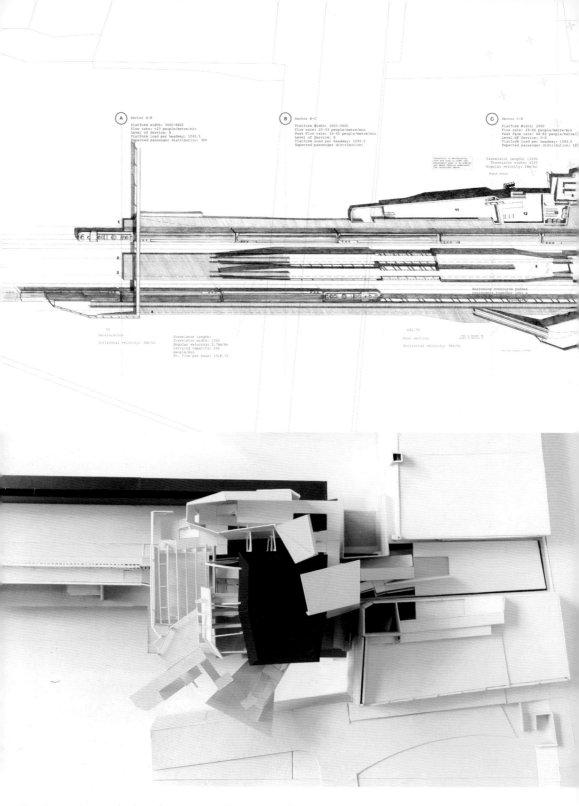

Top: Kaowen Ho, *Long Island Intercity Transport Terminus*, Bottom Left: Michael Pugh, *Coney Island Fireworks Laboratory*, Bottom Right: Theo Games Petrohilos, *Bankers' Refuge*.

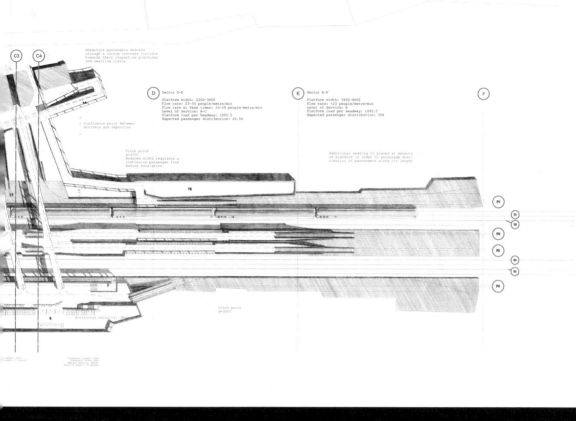

Departure passengers descend
through a narrow concrete corridor
towards their respective platforms
and awaiting trains

D Sector D-E

Platform width: 2000-3400
Flow rate: 23-33 people/metre/min
Flow rate at Peak times: 33-49 people/metre/min
Level of Service: B-C
Platform load per headway: 1093.5
Expected passenger distribution: 22.5%

E Sector E-F

Platform width: 3400-6600
Flow rate: <23 people/metre/min
Level of Service: A
Platform load per headway: 1093.5
Expected passenger distribution: 30%

F

Confluence point between
Arrivals and Departure

Pinch point
w=2020
Reduced width regulates a
continuous passenger flow
before escalators

Additional seating is placed at extents
of platform in order to encourage distribution of passengers along its length

Pinch point
w=3000

Horizontal velocity:

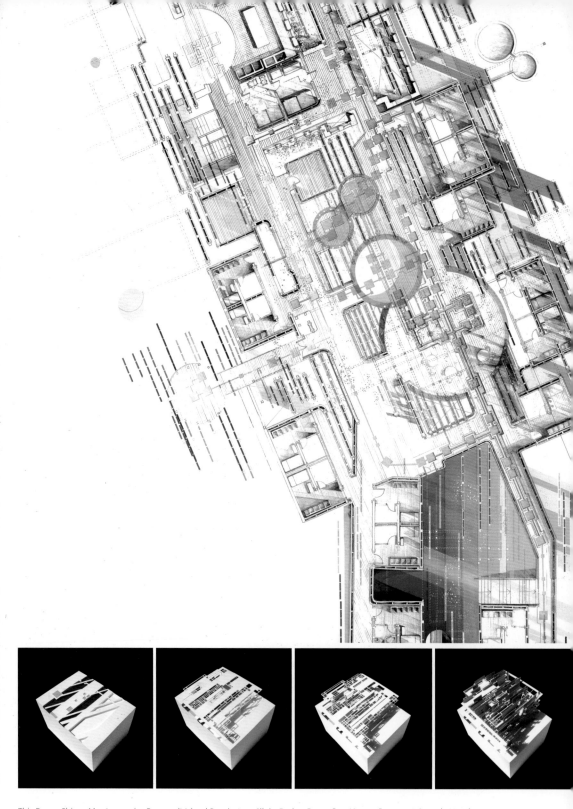

This Page: Chiara Montgomerie, *Roosevelt Island Respiratory Clinic*, Facing Page: Ben Hayes, *Resonant Capsule Hotel*

BSc Unit 9

Yr2: Khalid Al Sugair; Nichola Barrington-Leach; Laura Brayne; Alexander Holloway; Yee Y Lau; Christopher Leung; Rhianon Morgan-Hatch; Linlin Wang; Clarissa Yee
Yr3: Paul Leader-Williams; Keong L Lim; Louise Robson; Jack Spencer Ashworth; Richard A Sprogis; Tim Yue.

Alter Ego

The term alter ego; (Latin for "the other I") coined by psychologists in the 19th century and popularised by the psychoanalytic movement, is said to refer to a second self or double psychological life. The alter ego is often used to describe identical characters within literature and film and is also used as a tool to analyse the relationship between a character and it's author. Alter ego is the creation of an imagined other self, making a parallel or imagined universe, or second life, both absent and present. The architecture of alter ego explores multiple identities and layered memories of place. We investigate the spaces of heterotopia, that are neither here nor there, spaces that are simultaneously physical and metaphysical. In exploring the multifaceted psychological, literary, artistic and cultural dimensions of alter ego, Unit 9 aims to delineate a non linear architecture of duality. We investigate duplicated and mirrored spaces as a means of posing questions of scale and authenticity. The concept of alter ego also encompasses ideas about the relationship between an original and its copy and of parallel spaces thus creating two figures within a figure, two references within a reference, or two cities within a city. We focus our spatial explorations of alter ego on Istanbul or Constantinople, which has historically been a city of otherness to Northern European Capitals and which marked an edge of Europe a point of confluence for Europe and Asia. Istanbul forms the site for the main building project this year.

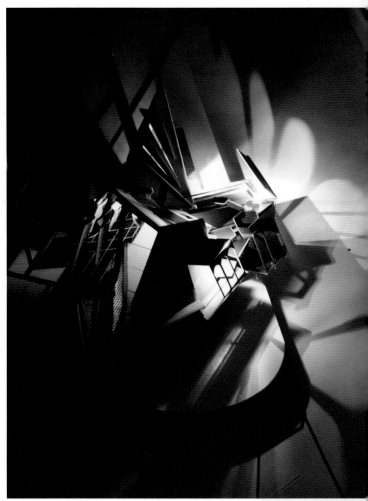

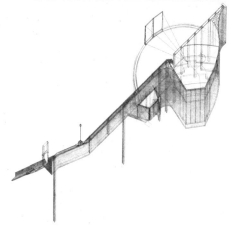

Top and bottom right: Tim Yue. Bottom left: Alexander Holloway.

Max Dewdney and Chee-Kit Lai

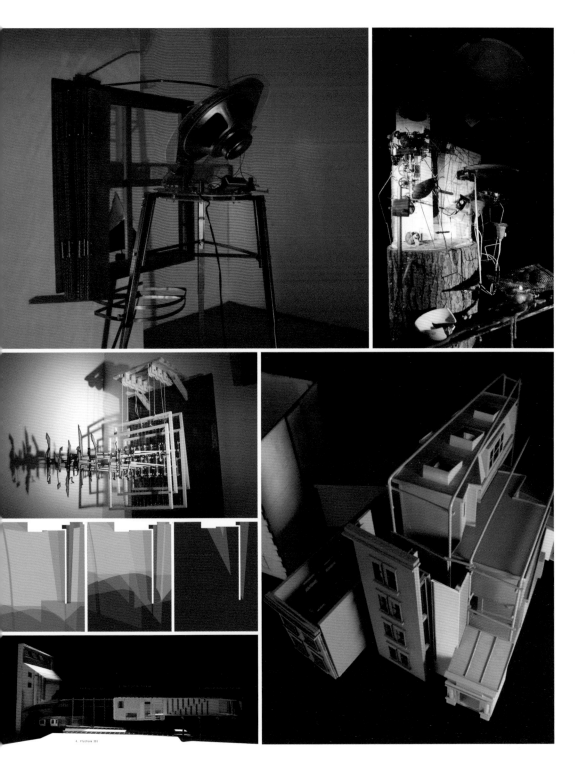

Clockwise from top left: Alexander Holloway, Khalid Al Sugair, Paul Leader-Williams, Keong L Lim,
Jack Spencer Ashworth, Yee Y Lau.

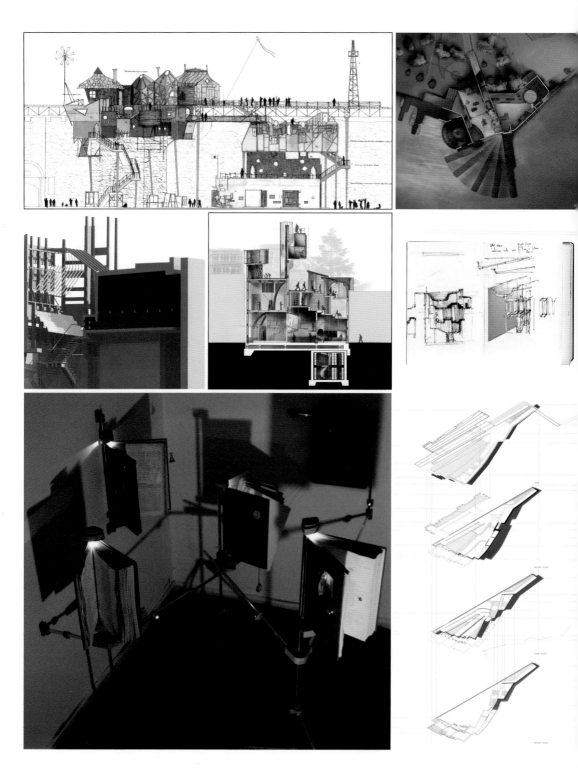

Top left to right: Rhianon Morgan-Hatch, Christopher Leung. Middle left to right: Jack Spencer Ashworth, Linlin Wang, Nichola Barrington-Leach. Bottom left to right: Linlin Wang, Nichola Barrington-Leach.

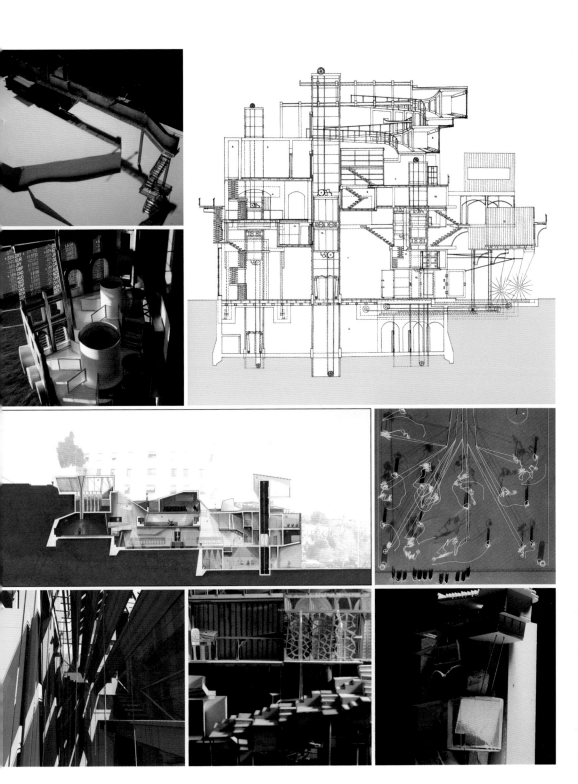

Clockwise from top left: Alexander Holloway, Yee Y Lau, Clarissa Yee, Laura Brayne, Louise Robson,
Jack Spencer Ashworth, Clarissa Yee, Richard A Sprogis.

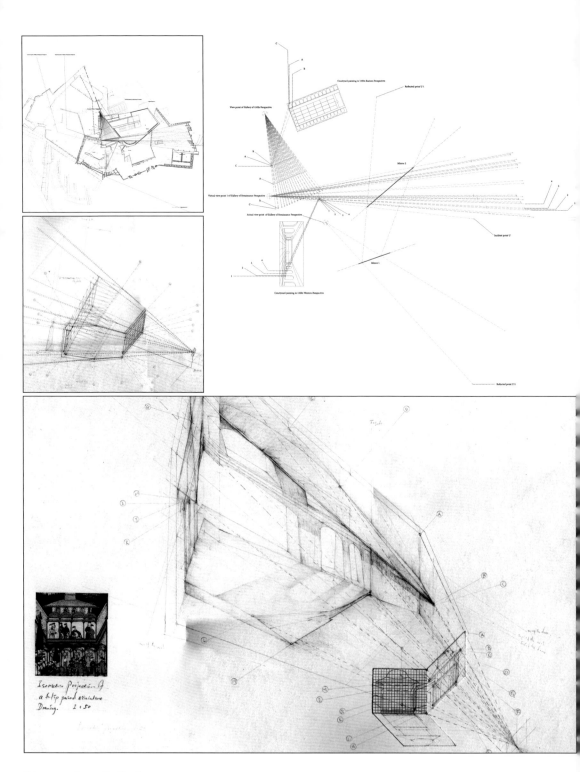

This page and opposite: Tim Yue.

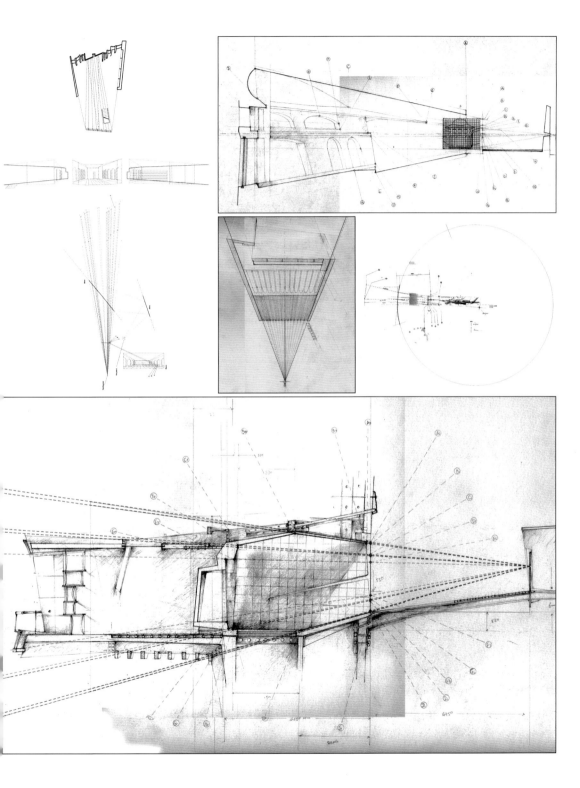

BSc Architectural Studies

Yr. 2: Emma Bass, Pasara Chaichanavichkij, Emilia Hadjikyriakou, Katie Hatch, Matilda Keane, Lydia Lim, Laura Neil, Mei Neoh, Ed Pearson, Charlotte Reynolds, Jingru Zhang.
Yr. 3: Charmian Beedie, Stephanie Chung, Joanne Clark, Lucinda Dye, Will Henderson, Pheobe Lewis, Tingting Qin, Jenni Young, Brian Yen (affiliate).

The Bartlett offers a BSc (Hons) in Architectural Studies. This is a unique course that allows students to follow modules within the Bartlett in conjunction with modules in other departments of UCL. The programme has been running since 2002-3 and now has over 60 graduates and a well-established track record. Graduates have gone on to postgraduate studies and professional careers in a wide variety of fields including: journalism, landscape design, lighting design, documentary film, conservation, photography, print-making, arts education and management, event management, planning, law, marketing and the media, property valuation, construction management, the charity sector, and heritage institutions. They have pursued further studies at places from the Royal College of Art to ETH in Zurich as well as in various UCL Masters programmes.

The great strength of the AS programme is its multidisciplinarity: students are able to tailor their own course of study to suit their particular interests and future postgraduate and career plans. It suits highly motivated, independent students who are interested in architecture and urban studies and who wish to take advantage of electives on offer elsewhere in UCL. Popular choices are Art History, Management, Language, Economics, History, Philosophy, Mathematics, Anthropology, Law, Archaeology, Biology, and Geography.

There are two specially tailored course modules for Architectural Studies students within the Bartlett. The Dissertation is an independent written project focusing on an architectural subject of a student's choice and resulting in an investigative in-depth written report. Project X is an independent creative project in which students research an architectural idea or series of ideas through visual and other architectural media – including drawing, photography, model-making, casting, sound, film, new digital media, installation and performance – in conjunction with a short creative written piece. Examples from both Dissertation and Project X are reproduced on the following pages.

Project X

Yr 2: Emma Bass, Pasara Chaichanavichkij, Neil Grayshon, Emilia Hadjikyriakou, Matilda Keane, Laura Neil, Ed Pearson, Charlotte Reynolds, Jingru Zhang Yr 3: Charmian Beedie, Stephanie Chung, Joanne Clark, Lucie Dye, William Henderson, Phoebe Lewis, Tingting Qin, Jennifer Young.

Project X aims to help students build a creative and reflective practice of their own. It enables them to undertake a mode of working that particularly interests them and an independent practice-based project in which they can research and pursue a subject of their preference. Students are asked to think of architecture in interdisciplinary ways, explore alternative approaches to design and situate their work within a broader cultural context. The work is developed in conjunction with a short written piece. A series of key questions confront students at different stages of the year concerning the nature of their practice, the contribution of their work to the broader field of architecture, the originality of their project, and the selection of appropriate media for the ideas pursued.

For their inspirational lectures and workshops warmest thanks to David Cross, Brandon LaBelle, Lea Catherine Szacka, and Victoria Watson.

For their constructive comments special thanks to our guest critics: Katerina Alexiou, Mary Dalton, Thomas-Bernard Kenniff, Yat-Ming Loo, Barbara Penner, Ben Sweeting, Nina Vollenbroker and Theodore Zamenopoulos.

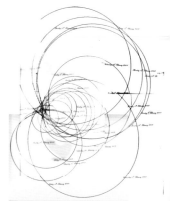

BSc Architectural Studies Director: Barbara Penner

Project X Tutor: Katherine Bash
Project X Coordinator: Yeoryia Manolopoulou

The Queen's Tobacco Pipe — "a furnace in which unadulterated tea and ... spices ... and other confiscated goods used to be burned"

Scents of spices and tobacco diffuse into the air

"The fire in the furnace is fed day and night with condemned goods"

1:50

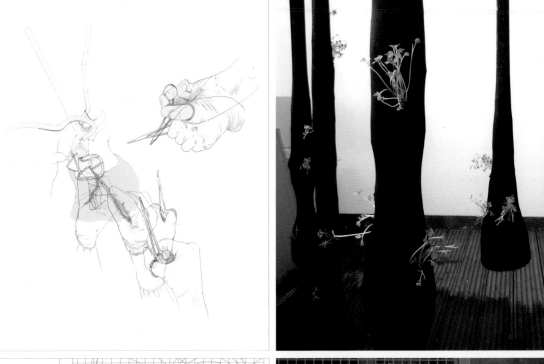
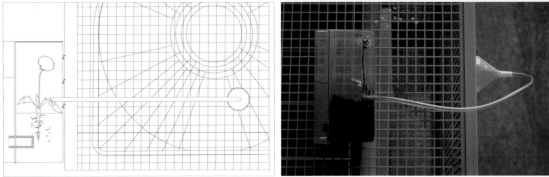

Clockwise from top left: Joanne Clark, Jennifer Young, Phoebe Lewis, Charmian Beedie, Phoebe Lewis.

This page: William Henderson.

Dissertation

Yr. 2: Mei Neoh. Yr. 3: Joanne Clark, Lucinda Dye, Will Henderson, Pheobe Lewis, Jenni Young, Brian Yen (affiliate)

The Dissertation enables students to undertake an independent research project of 10,000 words. The emphasis is on conducting original research and producing an in-depth written report, supported by appropriate visual and textual documentation. This course is taught through individual or small group tutorials, supplemented by occasional seminars and group meetings. The aims of the Dissertation are to enable students to conduct primary research, to think critically about issues with architectural implications, and to develop and showcase practical writing and presentation skills.

Joanne Clark
Shopping in London: engendering gendering

A significant fraction of Westfield London is the high-end retail area named The Village, comprising of 40 designer outlets out of the 265 across the whole mall. The separation of this group of 'premium' shops automatically gives them a sense of exclusivity beyond the high price tags accompanying the designer names, an integration not as 'seamless' as suggested. The Village is marketed as a more glamorous section of the mall and the price difference in luxury goods naturally extends to the architecture. The main architectural difference is its curves: eight-metre tall panels of curved (and presumably costly) glass sweep across the facades of the stores contrasting the glass facades of the rest of the centre which are predominantly linear. These curves are also manifest in the staircase between the two floors this area inhabits, the open spaces between these floors, the balconies that surround them and the large elaborate glass chandeliers hanging

from further curved reliefs in the ceiling - designed by Replica, the company who makes 'hyper-realistic' food models for Selfridges. The immense size of the glass facade is somewhat imposing reinforcing the sense of exclusivity.

The reflective surfaces of the vast glass facades and the highly polished marble floor are reminiscent of the Art Deco style, moreover, are evocative of 1920s ocean liners that capitalised on the new popular style of the time. Ocean liners were built with an emphasis on comfort, creating the most lavish spaces possible in what was the most technologically advanced and fashionable mode of commercial long distance travel of the time. The ocean liner came to symbolise luxury, glamour and convenience, exactly the qualities Westfield London, and principally The Village, wishes to exude. [...]

In considering gender in shopping, we may ask to what extent The Village is gendered. Gendering in architecture often stems from physical comparisons with the biological body: phallic towers are commonly associated with men and conversely soft, curved interiors are connected to women. The latter qualities are all evident in The Village, so this notion would interpret The Village as gendered female. This is furthered by the designated use of this section of the centre in particular, as a place for the consumption of luxury commodities, something I have

already discussed as being a naturalised role of women through history, namely middle class women. Not only this, the soft lighting radiating from the ceiling is pink. Pink is a colour which in western society has been culturally coded as feminine and specifically, a 'passive, innocent... immature' femininity through its connotations of 'girly' and female infants. On one hand this might be understood as a playful quality; however, this might also be interpreted as associating the space with 'passive' and 'immature' behaviour, a frequent criticism of luxury commodity shopping.

Looking at the materiality, the reflective qualities of the vast glass, one cannot escape the notion of the boudoir, a historically female gendered space; 'a woman's private room', as the cabinet was to the male. Again, a space not only associated with women, but upper class women who could afford such additional rooms in their homes. Jean-Francois de Bastide's novel La Petite Maison is a story of seduction, a fictitious tale in which the marquis de Tremicour wagers he can seduce a woman. However, it is the house, the architecture and the interior, which is the active seducer in the story not the marquis. There are endless similarities between this space of seduction and Westfield, such as 'all the walls were hung with mirrors... and hung with chandeliers'. Thus, the shopping mall uses the same techniques to a space of seduction, tempting the female consumer to part with her money through these devices. Looking at oneself at length in a mirror has associations with femininity, as does the applying of make-up, an activity predominantly gendered female. In Meaghan Morris' 'Things to Do with Shopping Centres', she writes:

Like department stores before them... [shopping centres] are described as palaces of dreams, halls of mirrors, galleries of illusion ... and the fascinated analyst becomes identified as a theatre critic, reviewing the spectacle, herself in the spectacle, and the spectacle in herself.

The glass shop facades give a total transparency allowing the consumer to see deep inside shops. The user is

Coordinator: Barbara Penner

constantly presented with a panorama of consumables, multiple images layered through glass and onto it reflections. The shop becomes this gallery of illusion as Morris suggests above. If this allusion to the theatre is applied to the shopping centre, where the divide between stage and audience is blurred by design, the purpose might be to make the consumer feel a part of the glamour. It is a form of flattery playing on human desire, similar to the displays in shops. These encourage the shopper to partake in a mentally constructed fantasy whereby they imagine owning the consumables. The consumer may identify with the attractive architecture and in seeing oneself in the architecture become the same. Thus, if you can identify with a more affluent architecture, you could be seduced into behaving more affluently. Iain Sinclair described this as becoming carried away as you are 'overwhelmed by excess of consumer opportunity' which is suggestive of why the popular image of the shopping for the middle-class Victorian female came to often be described as a 'wasteful, indulgent, immoral and disorderly pastime'.

Will Henderson
"Real Irreality: The Digital Truth of Architectural Photography Imagery"

The photograph serves to make permanent that one moment of hyper-readiness for action – precision timed, all-systems-go – that split-second vortex towards which months and years of human effort have been funnelled. The building, photographed in this way, becomes indelibly inscribed with its crowing moment of technological perfection; no subsequent interpretation can undermine its varnished truth.

The photograph serves to make permanent that one moment of hyper-readiness for action – precision timed, all-systems-go – that split-second vortex towards which months and years of human effort have been funnelled. The building, photographed in this way, becomes indelibly inscribed with its crowing moment

of technological perfection; no subsequent interpretation can undermine its varnished truth.

- Janet Abrams, *Site Work*, 1991.

The multitude of newspapers, magazines and guidebooks, which flood our modern society, ensure that a photograph is most often our first and sometimes, only experience of a building. Whether it is the latest high-tech, glass-clad, cloud-reaching tower to amend a city's skyline or a small grass-roofed wind-powered house on the shores of southeast England, there is little doubt that many of those who experience it, experience it first and quite possibly, solely, through photographs.

Yet even if a photograph is our only experience, we still believe we have gained a certain understanding of the architecture in question, a confidence to judge its aesthetics and comment on its success as an attractive addition to the cityscape or as a useful example of sustainable living. Somehow we believe that these photographs tell it like it is – literal copies of the built environment, framed into a four-by-five-inch rectangle and delivered to us untouched and saturated with reality. Indeed, such is the strength of these depictions that they become the reality to which we constantly refer: as the historian Beatriz Colomina explains, "even when in the presence of an actual building, visitors inevitably see it through the lens of the images they already know".

It can nevertheless be a strange feeling when we witness in real life, architecture that we have become acquainted with through photographs. For what we know – or now, knew – was different. It looked untouched, unspoiled, basking endlessly in a perfect light, an ethereal hue cast over its immaculate surface and it seemed somehow separate from its lesser surroundings, an unearthly calm allowing an unhindered view. It is a moment we can never experience; an optimum one that lies solely in the world of architectural photography – the moment existing between a building's completion and its inhabitation. The truth with which we are almost certainly faced therefore is that of something much more human, something altogether more ordinary.

Jenni Young
Architectura Vocabulorum: "an architecture of words"

Passage

The word 'passage' to me suggests possibility. It does this because it is suggestive of movement. Just as dust suggests an architecture that moves, so does passage, but, unlike dust, which is an object of movement itself, the word 'passage' suggests the movement of people.

Architecture is not a static object, we move through it, and it encourages movement. Although we fix our identity to places, our 'hometown', our 'bedroom', we are much more transient. We spend our days moving through architecture, and exploring the building environment. The idea of a flow of movement transfers to the concept of passage as it has been used in architectural discourse. 'Passage', both the space and concept, often forms the setting for a discussion about feminist space.

Despite expecting architectural dictionaries to deal with the most architectural of all three words I have chosen, the only reference was in the *Dictionary of Urbanism*, which referred to the nineteenth-century arcades of Paris. But just looking at the word we can form the link between passages to the Parisian arcades and back to Jane Rendell's rendering of passages as gendered spaces. The image that words create, in this case a passage as either a space of transition and possibility or a dark and dangerous place to be avoided at night, is not always so literal. The abstract image of the passage as we each imagine it can be the focus of architectural thought; the possibilities in this case are endless.

Bartlett architecture students undertake their studies in the full range of architectural subject matter and enquiry. Professional Studies, History & Theory and Technology are all explored both implicitly within the design process and explicitly in specialised and comprehensive stand-alone modules.

Through this integrated and extensive approach to architectural education, students experience all aspects of architecture, from the abstract and ideational, social and cultural, rational and pragmatic, to the managerial and economic.

Professional Studies & Part 3

From day one, architecture students are asked to question the role and function of the architect. The range of practices which graduates later join is as diverse as the individuals who arrive at the school - and in the intervening period, preconceptions are continually challenged through encounters with fellow students, the teachers (many of whom run their own practices) and numerous visiting experts.

Students' own ambitions and career aspirations are nurtured within the framework of innovative professional studies courses, as well as through informal advice on practice and employment.

BSc Architecture Year 1 students work with planning and construction management students on the 'Production of the Built Environment' course, which introduces the various individual and organisations involved in the process of producing buildings, as well as broader political, social and economic forces. In BSc Year 3 students take the 'Preparing for Practice' course which equips them for life in an architectural practice during their subsequent Year Out. The Year Out course itself continues the connection with the Bartlett and provides support and monitoring of practical experience through individual tutorials and a series of themed lecture days.

The Design Realization course in the Diploma Architecture Year 4 brings together professional practice, construction and technology though a unique relationship between individual design units, practice tutors, consultants and visiting lecturers.

The Part 3 Certificate in Professional Practice and Management is to open to non-Bartlett students and is truly international, attracting students from over 25 different countries. The course prepares students for registration as an architect through a comprehensive course of lectures, seminars and tutorials. A unique virtual learning environment enables students working in offices to remain closely connected to the Bartlett, and to form networks among themselves for self-directed learning.

Susan Ware
Director of Professional Studies

History and Theory

Architectural history and theory is a staging post, a provisional place of reflection, a continual project. And it is omnipresent – every architect, every historian, every theorist, knowingly or not, uses some intersection of history and theory every time they design, document, discuss or speculate.

At the Bartlett, architectural history and theory interjects at all levels, from introductions to architectural analysis, from encounters with buildings to the elaboration of critical practices, from public discussions to individually focused research projects.

Prof. Iain Borden
Director of Architectural History & Theory

Year 3 Dissertation

Joel Cady: The Impossible Dream. The London 2012 Olympics as a a site for the prohection of decontextualised futures.

This paper explores the role of decontextualised futures as projected by the public relations campaign for the London 2012 Olympics.

The London 'Olympic Park' – including the Olympic Village and most of the main sports venues – will be sited in the Lower Lea Valley, on the eastern edge of London. My focus here is on this large area, which has been completely enclosed and redeveloped. The redevelopment has been accompanied by an extensive public marketing campaign which relies heavily on images of a supposed future, both during and after the games. This highly visual public relations strategy has been an important part of the redevelopment process so far. The marketing images conspicuously lack any urban context. They depict abstracted representations of a gleaming new future, with no reference to its siting in an existing city: the Olympic dream is depicted as it could be in any 'world city', at any time in the recent past or the near future.

The Impossible Dream
The London 2012 Olympics as a site for the projection of decontextualised futures
Joel Cady

Year 4 Article

Dean Walker: The Suburban Dream. Look Closer...

"My name is Lester Burnham. This is my neighbourhood. This is my street. This is my life. I'm 42 years old and in less than a year I'll be dead. Of course, I don't know that yet, and in a way, I'm dead already." (American Beauty, 2006).

Lester Burnham's tragic tale of his daily reality, recounts the problem of a society consumed by the biopolitical nature of American suburbia. In this context, the 'suburban dream' is shown to be instigated by a power that is derived from Michael Foucault's investigation of power in imperial France, and is therefore an integral part of the 'cultural logic of late capitalism'.

This article examines the effective control suburban biopolitics has upon its population, with reference to two exemplary movies: American Beauty (2006) and The Truman Show (1998). I use the concept of biopolitics from Michael Hardt and Antonio Negri's Empire (2000), and postmodernity from Fredric Jameson's Postmodernism or the Cultural Logic of Late Capitalism (1991). The article argues that the suburban biopolitics of empire portrays an image of effective control which merely serves as a veil concealing the reality of postmodern fragmentation and dysfunction, and concludes that this crisis calls for utopian interventions on behalf of the individual subject.

Technology

Technological production defines a substantial part of contemporary culture – from clothing to music to architecture. The social experience of architecture is predicted by the way we, as architects, construct our environment in both a physical and a conceptual sense.

The Bartlett is fortunate. We are able to draw on 'cutting edge' experts to help our students explore these issues in design from BSc Year 1 to Diploma Year 5. Students work with drawings, texts, models, physical experiments and 1:1 installations.

Prof. Stephen Gage
Director of Technology

Harriet Redman – Technical Prize

When an idea is tested beyond the evident then curious and beautiful outcomes are born. Harriet's technical submission is testament to this. Her erudite and incisive investigation of concrete pier and fibreglass shell construction methods leads to a highly imaginative and entirely convincing architectural proposal.

Joel Cady – Making Buildings Award

This is a new award donated by the lecturers' of the Making Building Lecture series to further develop a quality idea in built form. Joel's exceptional idea of a three phase European Convention Centre in Istanbul uses Pyrotechnics, Latent seed germination and controlled concrete erosion together in a detail that is designed to adapt to the buildings requirements.

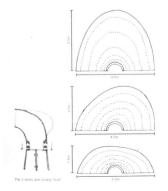

Harriet Redman

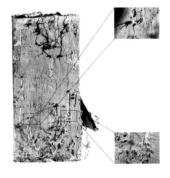

Joel Cady

Dip/MArch Unit 10

Yr 4: Byron Bassington, Lik San Chan, Barry Cho, Wing Man Cheung, Sulawan Isvarphornchai, Janice Lee, Geraldine Ng, Dean Walker.
Yr 5: Pascal Bronner, Jacqueline Chak, Lucy Jones, Seung Hyun Kang, YongZheng Li, Okan Kaleli, Sarah Mui.

Connections

Four interlocking stories all connected by a single gun converging at the end to reveal a complex and tragic story of the lives of humanity around the world and how we truly are not all that different. *Babel*, Guillermo Arriaga. Virginia Woolf's *"Mrs. Dalloway"*, interconnected with the lives of a 1950s housewife and a new-millennium publisher; one is writing it, one is reading it, and one is living it. *The Hours*, Michael Cunningham. A poetry of places in a global network - where human activity is explored through the places and structures we inhabit, and the routes that penetrate and connect them. *Frozen Sky*, Langlands & Bell. In an isolated Danish village, Babette prepares the feast of a lifetime with ingredients connecting to past lives and the rest of the world. *Babette's Feast*, Karen Blixen. In Ersilia, the inhabitants stretch strings from the corners of the houses, white or black or gray or black-and-white according to whether they mark a relationship of blood, of trade, authority, agency. *Invisible Cities*, Italo Calvino. The explorations of connection read beyond the apparent and suggested subtle personal readings of the theme while engaging in creative and intellectual expressions for new architecture.

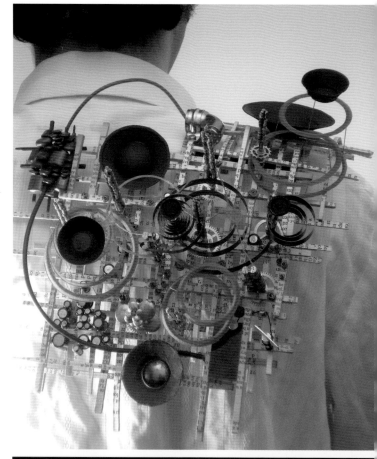

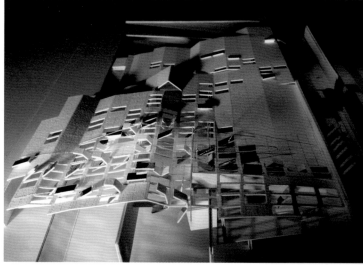

cj Lim and Bernd Felsinger

Top: Lucy Jones, *Burdensome City*. Bottom: Jacqueline Chak, *Golden Refraction*.

Clockwise from top left: Sulawan Isvarphornchai, *1630 at Marylebone Park*; Lik San Chan, *The House of Gossip*; Dean Walker, *Suburban Dream*; Okan Kaleli, *Phileas Fogg's Orchestral Landscape*.

Top: YongZheng Li, *Kurdish Homeland*. Bottom: Sarah Mui, *Garden of Impossibility*.

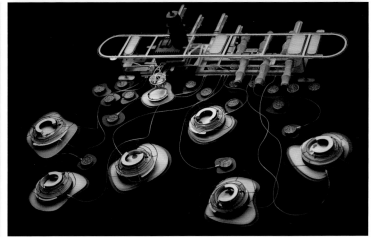

Clockwise from top left: Geraldine Ng, *Networking in Hampstead;* Byron Bassington, *Natural Un-natural Perfection;* Barry Cho, *Rear Window;* eung Hyun Kang, *Virgins' Island; Vivian Wing, Cut, Fold + Sew;* Janice Lee, Cambridge Circus.

Pascal Bronner, *Endless Laboratory: The Roots of Light*.

Pascal Bronner, *Endless Laboratory: Potatoes, Pixel Water and Pins.*

Dip/MArch Unit 11

Yr 4:Erin Byrne, Will Jeffries, Emily Keyte, Rae Whittow-Williams, Chris Wilkinson, Nicholas Wood. Yr 5: Margaret Bursa, James Davies, Tom Finch, Joel Geoghegan, Johan Hybschmann, Alex Kirkwood, Holly Lewis, Elin Lund, Itai Palti, Luke Pearson

Field Operations

Field operations, guidelines for actions, definitions of measures, are laid down by countless authorities endeavoring to control the effects of ensuing events. Neither the rural nor urban landscape is immune to the advance of these nervous reactions as we aim to fix on the moving target of an uncertain future. Our culture is voracious in its consumption and production of data. Typically, questions and answers are provided by its statistical manipulation.

Unit 11 is a laboratory for counter-programmes that will look at the hypothetical or physical notion of 'modeling' as a representation tool, as a systematic example to follow or simply as a description to assist predictions. For us, modeling in all its definitions, provides a framework where lines of enquiry are pursued through an iterative, inquisitive and imaginative process.

Thanks to Sam Jacob, John Lyall and Richard Stonehouse

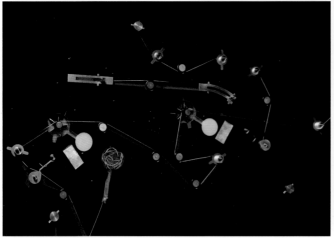

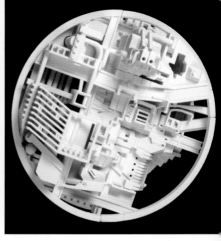

Laura Allen, Ana Monrabal-Cook and Mark Smout

This page: Itai Palti, *The Case for Curiosity, Film Studios Tel Aviv*. Facing Page: Clockwise from Top, Luke Pearson, *Thawing a Frozen Bureaucracy at UN Headquarters, New York*; Alex Kirwood, *Simulations of (a) Manhattan from Google Earth*; Joel Geoghagen, *Subterranean Hydro-Assemblage, Construction and Destruction on the US/Mexico border*.

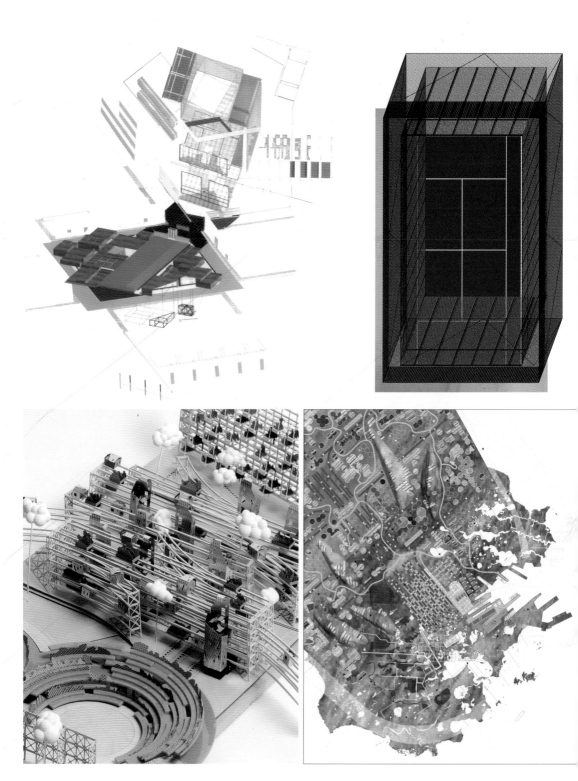

Clockwise from top: Tom Finch, *Exceptional White Architecture: A New American Embassy*; James Davies, *The Pioneer State, Remediation for Governor's Island, New York*; Holly Lewis, *Coney Island Refurbishment Village*.

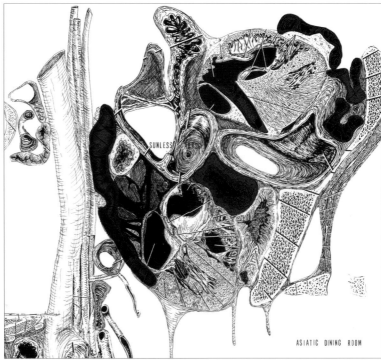

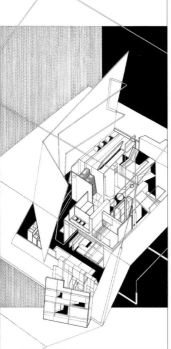

Clockwise from top: Chris Wilkinson, *A Sound Connection;* Rae Whittow-Williams, *Hallucinatory Architecture: The House of an Opium Eater;* Erin Byrne, *Thamesmeadian Simulacra: The Antiphonic Methodology;* Nick Wood, *747 LDN/NYC;* Will Jeffries, *The Survey of London*.

Margaret Bursa, *Escaping Landscape*. Top: *Sokolovna Landscape of Movement, Pier 54-56, New York*. Bottom: *The Green House, a manifestation of a the 'New Local' design principle for Zlin, Czech Republic.*

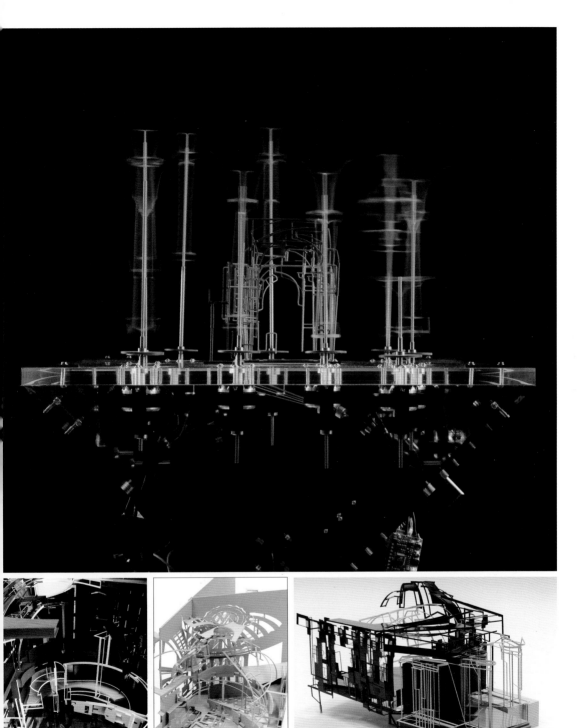

Johan Hybschmann, Top: *Recreating The Hermitage as a processional journey.*
Bottom: *Replicating a Replica, Redesigning the Federal Hall, New York.*

Dip/MArch Unit 12

Yr 4: Michael Wai Ho Hung, Villian Wing Lam Lo, Tom Noonan, Tom Reynolds, Erika Suzuki, Anna Vallius. Yr 5: Hakan Agca, Will Wai Lam Chan, James Church, Alex Hill, Kumiko Hirayama, David Potts, Francesca Wadia, Eva Willoughby, Alan Worn

"Perhaps when you cut into the present the future leaks out"

William Burroughs, *Origin and Theory of the Tape Cut-Ups*, 1976

During the 1950s writer William Burroughs and artist Brion Gysin experimented with a new writing technique dubbed the cut up and later the fold in. These experiments involved taking an initial text that was then cut up at random and re-arranged to create a new text. The aim of these experiments was to alter certain given assumptions of our understanding of time, history and memory. They were later used by Burroughs as a means to predict the future. This year Unit 12 used the principles of this technique and its emphasis on the cut, incision and juxtaposition, both conceptually and physically, in determining architectures, readings of site and understandings of architectural history.

Many of the most creative architects have looked to the past to imagine a future, studying an earlier architecture not to replicate it but to transform it, revealing its relevance to the present. Soane looked to ancient Greece, Mies admired Schinkel and the Smithsons absorbed the spirit of the picturesque. Modernism was supposedly based on the rejection of history but this is now known to be a myth. As a creative stimulus and narrative resource for twentieth-first century architecture, Unit 12 focuses on earlier centuries as well as those more recent. When everybody else is looking in one time and one place, it's always good to look elsewhere.

"Berlin is a laboratory. Its historical richness lies in the prototypical sequence of its models; neoclassical city, early metropolis, modernist test bed, war victim, Lazarus, Cold War demonstration, etc"

Fritz Neumeyer, 'OMA's Berlin: the polemic island in the city', 1990

This year the site for this investigation was Berlin.

Jonathan Hill, Elizabeth Dow, Matthew Butcher

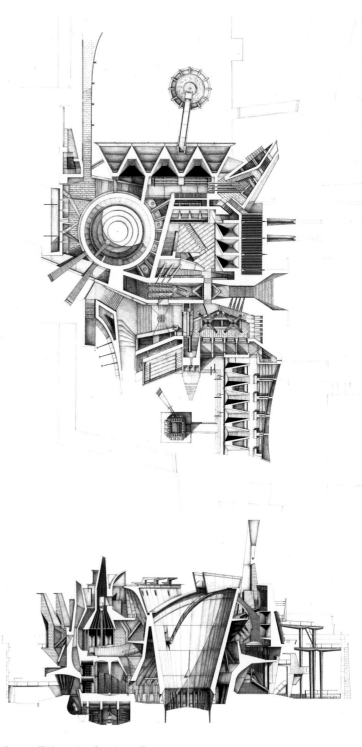

Above: Will Chan, *City of London Saffron Monastery.*

Above: Alex Hill, *The Alchemic Plant, Templehof.*

Clockwise from top left: James Church, *The Institute of Monumentality*; Erika Suzuki, *The Multicultural Cemetery, Tempelhof*; Hakan Agca, *The Carbon Capture Plant, super-critical furnace*; Anna Vallius, *Institute of Negotiation, Tempelhof*; James Church, *The Institute of Monumentality*; Lam Lo, *Sanatorium of Light, Water and Glass*.

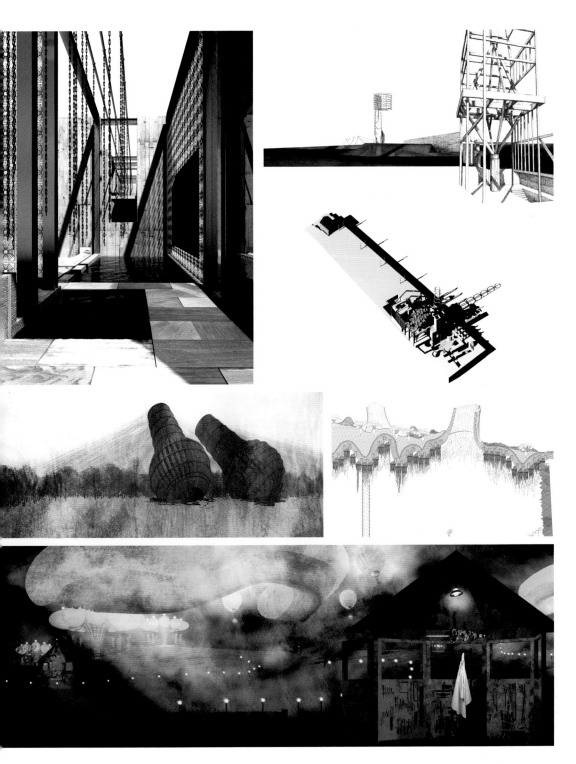

Clockwise from top left: Francesca Wadia, *The Halal Abattoir Berlin*; Tom Noonan, *The Ministry of Urbanism meets the Institute of De-Urbanism*; Tom Reynolds, *Recovery of Soul: Woodcut House*; Michael Wei Ho Hung, *The Seed Bank for Urban Agriculture*; Kumiko Hirayama, *Colour Farmada, Berlin Airlift*; Eva Willoughby, *The Weavers of Tempelhof*.

This page: David Potts, *The Museum of Illicit Culture*. Previous page: Alan Worn, *Curated Cultural Outpost*.

Dip/MArch Unit 14

Yr 4: Jonathan Craig, David DiDuca, Subomi Fapohunda, Helen Floate, Geraldine Holland, Eleanor Lakin, Chin Lye, Maxine Pringle, Guy Woodhouse. Yr 5: Michael Hammock, Sam McElhinney, Tetsuro Nagata, Chris Rodrigues, Declan Shaw, Andrew Usher, Nick Westby. MArch: Sam Walker.

The Real Thing

Unit 14 is experimental. Our aim is to support individual original work of exceptionally high quality within the framework of time-based architecture, architecture that is designed and understood in 4 dimensions. The unit explores how architecture can be designed to respond to change in the natural and man-made physical world and how this response can be perceived by observers. In 08-09 we specifically examined how architecture coexists with the natural world in the context of the city.

Some of the most successful Unit 14 projects have existed in the form of drawn and animated representation. However many important ideas about response and perception can only be examined by constructing "the real thing" i.e. 1:1 fragments or complete installations

FIELD TRIPS: In October the unit travelled to the Venice Biennale. The 2008 theme "Out There: Architecture Beyond Building" seemed particularly appropriate to the unit agenda. There was a second trip in April to Aarhus in Denmark when students presented their work at the School of Architecture and when Phil Ayres presented (and gained) his doctorate.

YEAR 4 - Beyond the Garden: Phoenix Gardens is an urban park in the centre of London. One of the main functions of the park is to provide a resource for local workers and local residents, especially urban children to interpret and enjoy the natural world. The brief is to design a building that can help observers learn about the natural world using every kind of device and design that can be invented. Students then developed a key idea to become a 1:1 installation.

YEAR 5 - Individual Agendas: Students in year 5 should have freedom to establish their own area of interest and their own approach to techniques of representation and testing.

Stephen Gage, Phil Ayres and Richard Roberts

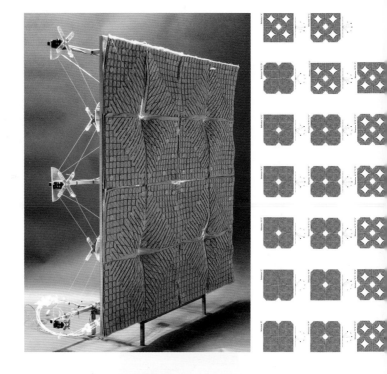

Top: Chin Lye, *Defoming*: A lattice skin, stiffened using rigid panels, is driven to display automatic and reactive behaviours. Bottom: Elie Lakin, *Electro Magnetic Typewriter*: The typewriter senses mobile phone messages and, using a set of cams and cranks, writes out a response. Following page, top row, Left: Dave Di Duca, *Building As Wall*: Dave's theme is to investigate the use of illusion in architecture. This is a proposal for a building that deploys out of a wall. Right: Jonty Craig, *Rise and Fall*: Jonty is working with the subtleties of level difference, to define specific interactions between objects and their observer/users.

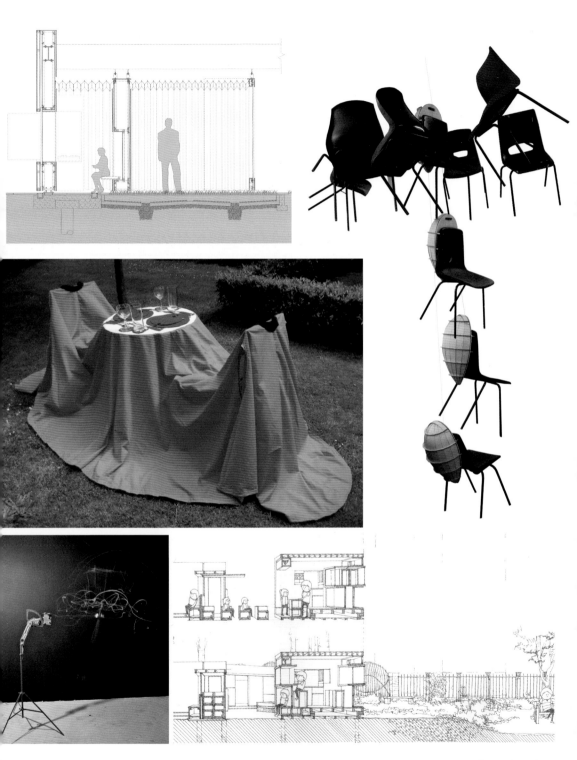

Centre row, Left: Max Pringle, *Wearable Buildings*: Max is following a long standing interest in the boundaries between architecture, furniture design and fashion. This project is part of a "collection" and proposes a wearable table cloth that is shared between two people. Bottom Row, Left: Subomi Fapohunda, *Fencester*: Subomi's theme is to invent buildings and objects that are choreographed to interact with each other and with observers. This is part of a series of studies into fencing. Right: Guy Woodhouse, *Cabinet Architecture*: Guy proposes an architecture of small things, where spaces are made (and unmade) by the incidental relationships between specially designed elements.

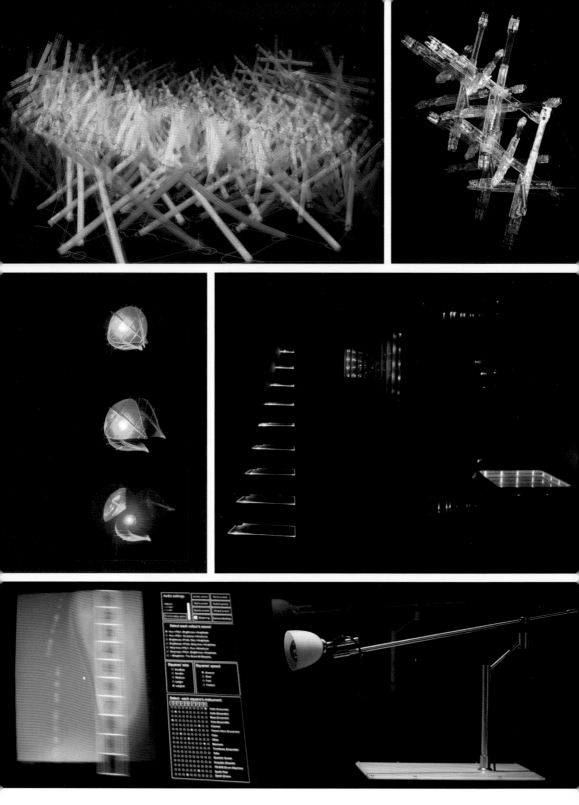

Top row: Nick Westby, *Parametric Tensegrity*: Nick studies reconfiguring tensegrity structures that change shape by changing spar length. Centre row, Left: Helen Floate: *'Bashful'*. This is a study of a shy interactive object. Right: Chris Rodrigues, *1 Lux World*: Chris takes the need for energy demand reduction and uses it as a spur to examine how safe and delightful night time worlds can be created with low light levels to give an architecture that avoids light pollution at a local and an urban scale. Bottom: Sam Walker, *Sound and Vision*: Sam has been working with Beau Lotto at UCL's Institute of Ophthalmology to construct objects that 'read' and 'play back' spaces and their inhabitants as sound in real time.

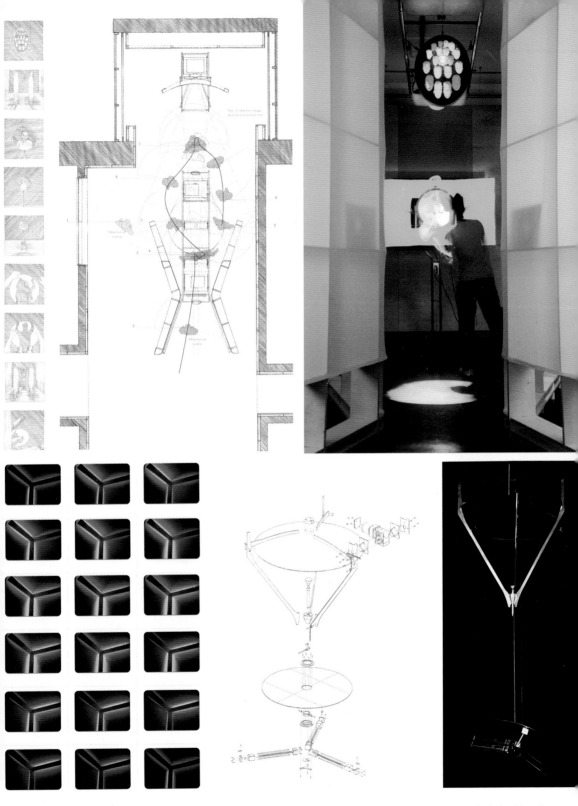

op: Tetsuro Nagata, *Memories of Self*: Tet explores 7 different interpretations of long and short term memory. His final installation is a memory theatre that detaches shadow, delays reflection and embeds observer image in a 1:1 array. Bottom Right & Centre: Andrew Usher, *The Intelligent Heliostat*: Andrew creates an intelligent heliostat that takes sunlight falling in a shaft nd directs it to cheer up individual users working in deep office plans. Bottom Left: Declan Shaw, *Waiting*: Declan creates a virtual 3D landscape traversed by virtual songbirds that respond o the actions of observers. The intention is to enhance moments of involuntary waiting, for example moments of waiting in hospitals and airports.

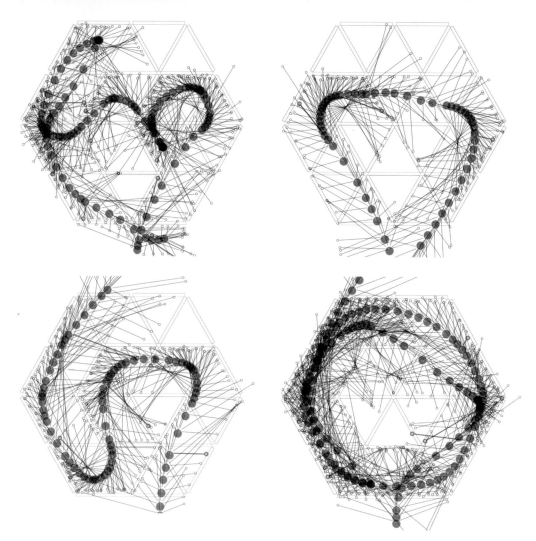

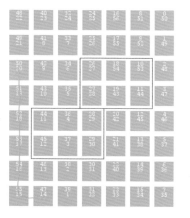
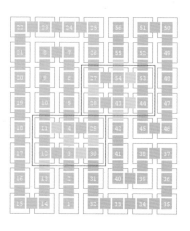
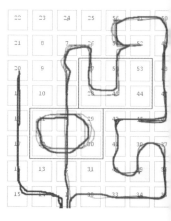

Sam McElhinney, *Switchable Labyrinths*: Sam develops a maze by switching between monocursal labyrinth forms. This is investigated digitally through the creation of intelligent maze forms populated by intelligent agents and then at 1:1 as an interactive maze.

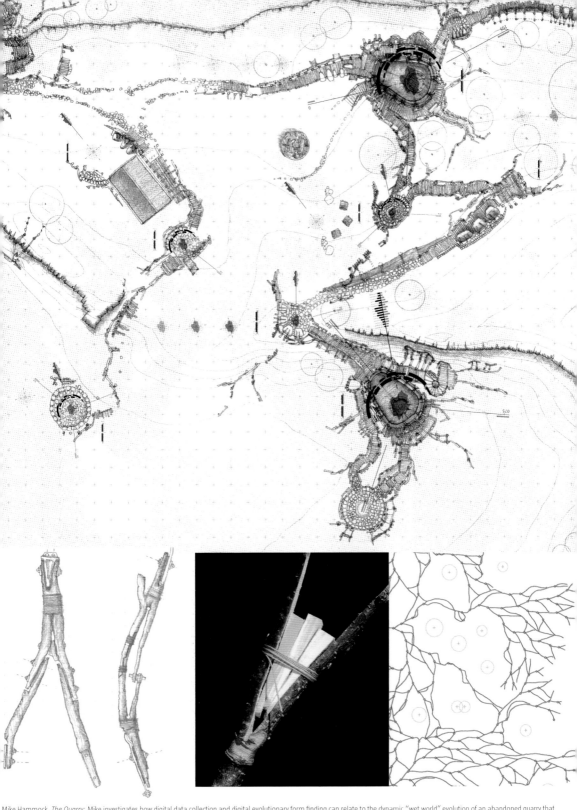

Mike Hammock, *The Quarry*: Mike investigates how digital data collection and digital evolutionary form finding can relate to the dynamic "wet world" evolution of an abandoned quarry that is used as a nature trail by local children.

Dip/MArch Unit 15

Year 4: Robert Brown, Richard Hardy, Yianni Kattirtzis, Louise Mackie, Keichi Matsuda, Natalie Wright. Year 5: Richard Bevan, Tom Johnson, Nancy NiBhriain, Lucas Tizard, Alexandra Thomson, George Thomson, Chao-Kai Wang. MArch: Michael Aling, Rammy Elsaadany, Dan Farmer, Soki So

Dedicated to the memory of J G Ballard [1930-2009]

This year Unit 15 questioned whether the utopian ambitions of the modernist project could still be maintained in light of the political, economic and environmental challenges that we now face. Global warming, terrorism, religious dogmatism, ethnic cleansing, economic meltdown and pandemic viral catastrophe are issues that we cannot ignore and yet we feel powerless, as individuals, to really address them.

It is obvious that the culture of 'business as usual', as pursued by many in the architectural profession, doesn't ring true. The architectural profession may still posit a future of 'bigness', a world of bright shiny mega-structures; of full employment, of equality and global harmony and unlimited growth and expansion, but should this view be met with incredulity? If the reality is not as rosy as it is pictured in the latest computer renderings from the 'corporate architectural complex', then what type of planet do we face?

The Near Future was an examination of a number of possible near futures, positing possible high-tech, low-tech and even no-tech alternatives to current prognostications.

Unit 15 would like to thank:

Matt Bowles, Paul Davies, Bastian Glassner, Peter Kidger, Andrew Kramer, Stefan Kueppers, Jeff Noon, Kim Quazi and FLACQ, Vesna Petrasin Robert, Simon Sellars, Simon Withers

Nic Clear and Simon Kennedy

Top Soki So, *Hong Kong Labyrinths* (chronogram), bottom Yianni Kattirtzis, *St Paul's Dome* (film still)

Top: Richard Hardy, **Eco-Commune** (film still).   Centre left: Keichi Matsuda, *Technocrat Retrofit of London* (film still).
Bottom: Rammy Elsadaany *Evo-Grid* (film still)

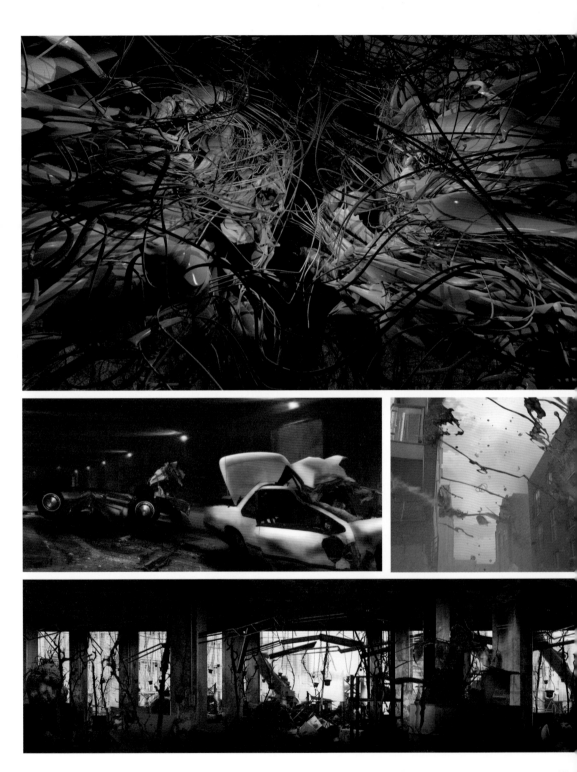

Top Lucas Tizard, *Prosthetic Architecture* (film still), centre left Dan Farmer *Prima Materia* (film still), centre right Daniel Wang, *Dirty Town* (film still), Alexandra Thomson, *Secondary Pleasures* (film still)

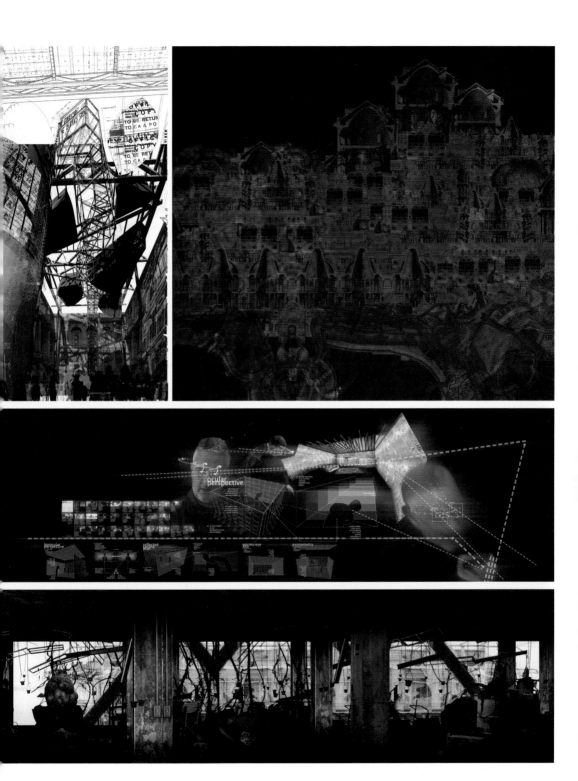

Top left Louise Mackie, *Free Exchange* (film still), top right Nancy NiBhriain *Haecceity* (collage section), centre Michael Aling, *ocular perspective* (chronogram).

Top Richard Bevan, *Syn Notation* (meso scale map)
bottom George Thomson, *The Resort* (film still)

Dip/MArch Unit 16

Yr 4:Ashley Ma, Ching Kan Chan, Daisuke Saito,Emily Yeung,Jinhyuk Ko,Jun Kundo,Spencer Tracey. Yr 5:Lok, Mark Martinez,Pernilla Ohrstedt,Ray Wang,Vicky Wong

Experimental Station [T.O.A.D]

Temporary / Obsolete / Abandoned / Desolate

An inside/outside architecture at the end of the Empire, the place to test and explore the emerging demands and needs of the 21st Century. We considered the car and the log as expressions of the same technology, hints of the ruins of the near future, a back catalogue to the past.

We find ourselves at the beginning of a new geological epoch the Anthropocen period, where the impact of our activities and technologies upon global systems and the physical environment are significant to rival those of nature.

We considered what it is to be experimental. Examining the origins and practice of the true amateur, whose restless musings were motivated by curiosity and an essential love to explore, reveal and understand the edges of meaning. Experimental was based on experience not on authority or mere conjecture.

The settings for our "anthropogeomorphological" investigation were Dungerness, Kent, a near desert landscape of paradox, then continental USA from Miami to Los Angeles.

We would like to thank Allford Hall Monaghan Morris Architects for their continued assistance with Design Realization, with special thanks to Philip Turner.

Simon Herron and Susanne Isa

Top: Ashley Ma, Bottom: Pernilla Ohrstedt.

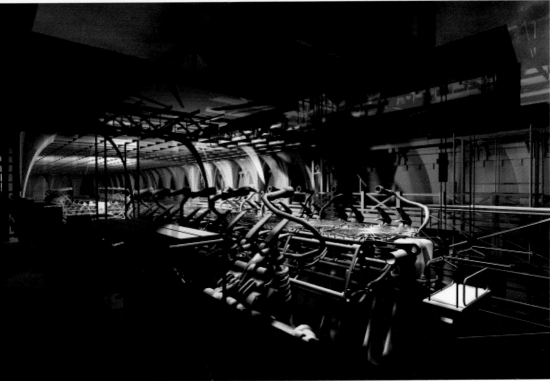

Top: Emily Yeung, Bottom: Ching Kan Chan.

This page and opposite : Pernilla Ohrstedt.

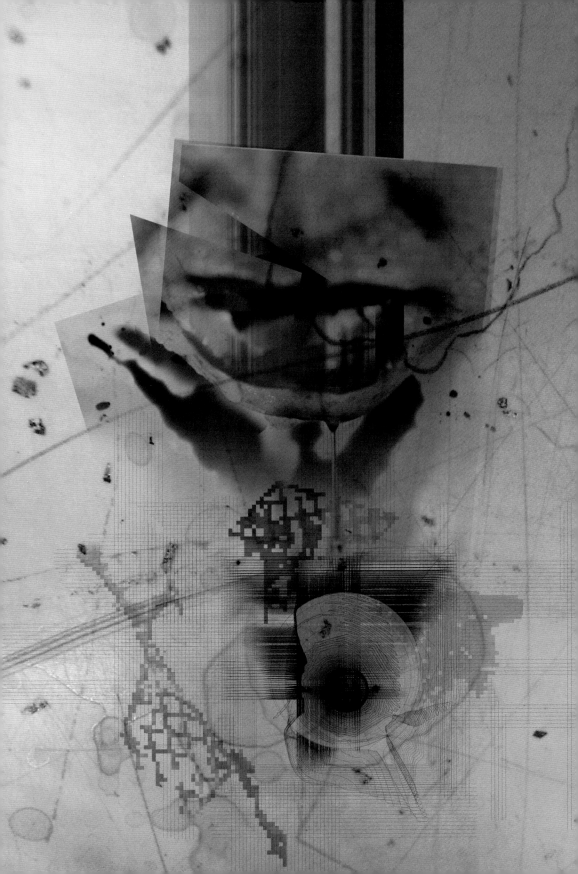

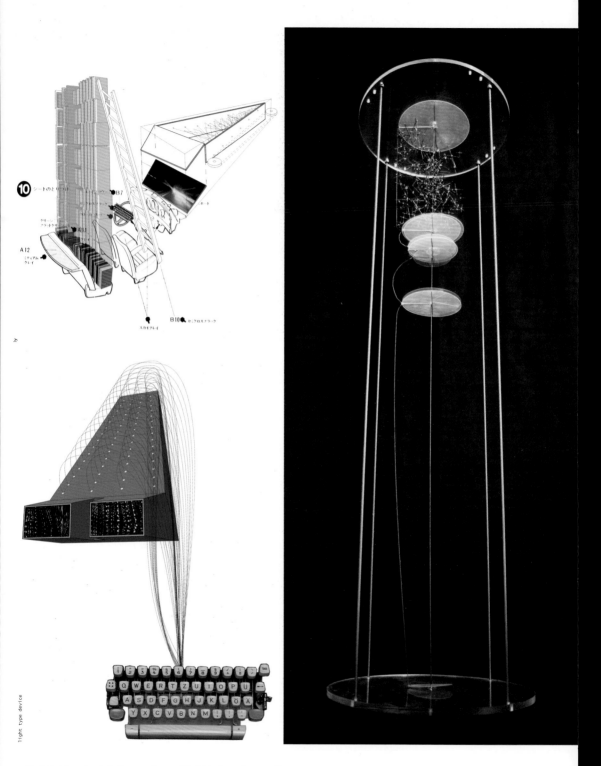

Clockwise from top left: Spencer Tracey, Mark Martinez, Spencer Tracey.

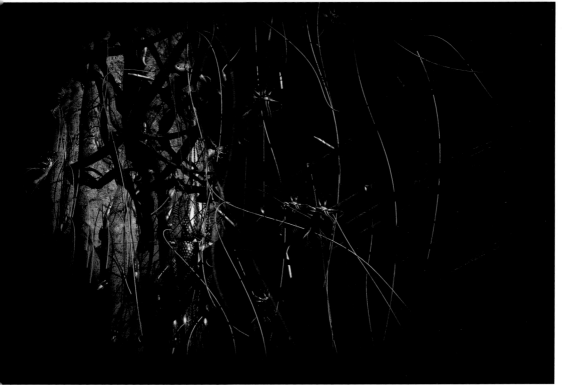

Top: Pernilla Ohrstedt. Bottom: Jinhyuk Ko.

Dip/MArch Unit 17

Yr 4: Tala Akkawi, Justine Bell, Sigrid Bylander, Alastair Crockett, Lino Egerman, Jonathon Horsfall, Katsura Leslie, Tatiana Malysheva, Thomas Winter. Yr 5: Robert Lunn, Brian Macken, Jack Pannell, Joshua Scott, James Stevens, Mitchiko Sumi, Dandi Zhang.

The Recovery Of The Real

[The city] is very ordinary, even worse than ordinary. But that is what it is, and I'm afraid that is what modernity is like when it is fresh. (Jeff Wall)

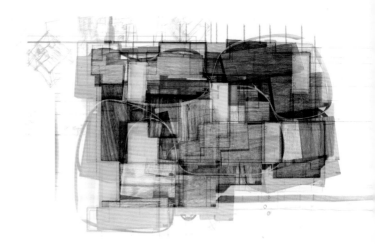

The city is under constant negotiation; it is provisional and contingent. It is 'the result of all our labours and errors'. We call it 'the real'. The recovery of the real in architecture has nothing to do with the pragmatics of ordinary practice. It involves a process of estrangement: stripping an action, a history or a place of anything that appears evident, familiar and understandable in order to arouse curiosity and astonishment about it instead. To recover the real for ourselves we need to discover the shock of it and communicate it through the public language of architecture. We question the extent to which students tend to depend on subjectivity, narrative and the figurative. A building which is truly public allows for a multitude of subjectivities. Close-up a building disappears.

Fieldtrip: Cape Town

Warmest thanks to Tim Allen-Booth, Julia Backhaus, Johan Berglund, Matthew Butcher, Nic Coetzer, Adam Cole, Sandra Coppin, James Daykin, Elizabeth Dow, Murray Fraser, Tilo Guenther, Christiana Ioannou, Katie Irvine, Jan Kattein, Iain Low, Paul Monaghan, Ana Monrabal-Cook, Ben Nicholls, Christos Papastergiou, Dean Pike, Mike Tonkin, Cindy Walters, Victoria Watson.

Niall Mclaughlin and Yeoryia Manolopoulou

This Page Top: Dandi Zhang *Calligraphy School , Beijing.*
This Page Bottom: Robert Lunn *Building School, Langa.*

This Page Top: James Stevens *The Tower of Robben Island.* This Page Bottom: Jack Pannell *Deconstructing Cape Peninsula University of Technology.*

This page and facing page: Michiko Sumi: *Timepiece, Reconstructing Robben Island.*

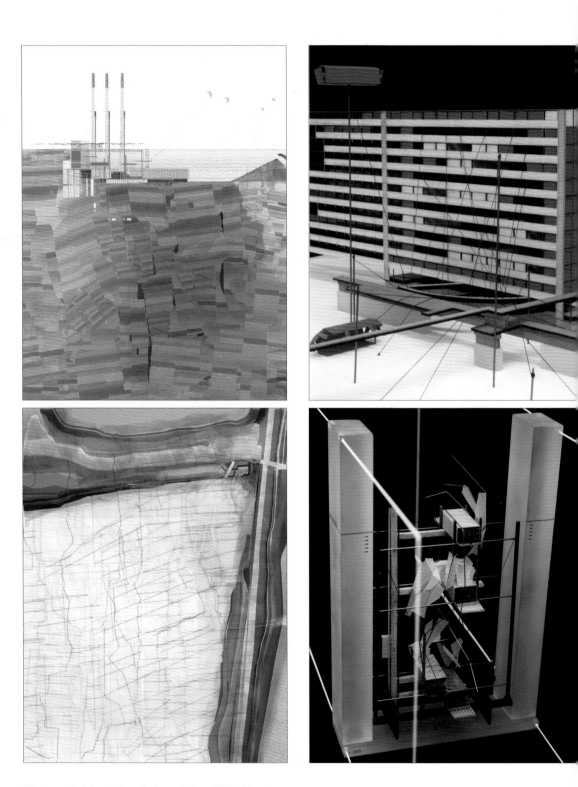

This Page Left: Brian Macken *The Remediation of Philippi Farming*.
Above Right: Joshua Scott *Compulsory Acquisition: Resisting Forced Removals in the Heygate Estate, London*.
Facing Page: Joshua Scott *Political Geology: South African Land Registry and Claims Court. Project sited in District Six*.

Dip/MArch Unit 18

Yr 4: Craig Brailsford, Quinton Clarke, Rory Donald, Christian Dorin, Harry Godfrey, Elizabeth Kirchner. Yr 5: Alice Cadogan, Christine Hui, Myoungjae Kim, George King, Koasis Fung, Daniel Madeiros, Thomas Mahon, Mark Nixon, Rachel Song, Miya Kate Ushida

Mutant!

Mutations provide the raw material for evolution, fuel for the Darwinian factory. They arise from random errors in translation of the genetic code and ensure the survival of living species subjected to unpredictable environmental changes. Architecture also faces the question of how to design for a changing world. Perhaps the answer is the same: paradoxically, the best way to develop robust design solutions may be to encourage mistakes in the transmission of established design rules, so that the architectural gene pool can become more diverse, enriched by freak mutations that may prove better adapted to new circumstances. The brief for this year stemmed from these fundamental considerations; it called for the exploration of architectural mutations, design processes that imitate Nature not so much in her forms but rather in her mode of operation.

The first exercise was to design a device investigating the working principles of mutations, a live demonstration of a mutation process. This initial exercise set the intellectual ambitions for the year and explored different ways in which these ambitions can be materialised. The architectural project following this conceptual exercise was set in Los Angeles, a city whose architectural gene pool, resulting from many distortions of its original genetic code, is particularly rich and exotic. This urban and architectural diversity, together with the complex cultural, socio-economic, physical and political milieu that underlies it, makes LA an ideal place to experiment with further mutations.

Colin Fournier and David Ardill

Top: Rory Donald, *Cymatic Landscape Symphonia*. Bottom: Harry Godfrey, *"Moment bien heureux" Escapism Clinic.*

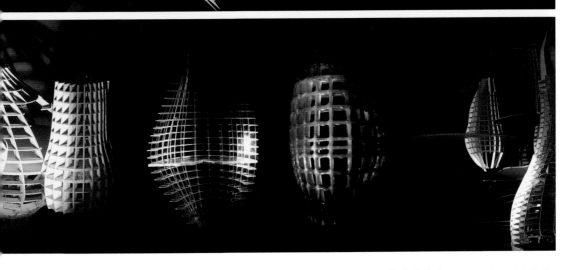

Top: Christian Dorin, *The Los Angeles Times*. Middle: Quinton Clarke, *The Body Boutique*. Bottom: Elizabeth Kirchner, *Kymaerica and stuff of other worlds*.

Top Left: Christine Hui, *Parsons School for Fashion Re-Development*. Top Right: Koasis Fung, *Vireality*. Bottom: Myoungjae Kim, *Paranoic Paradise; Acting School in LA.*

Top: Miya Kate Ushida, *The Act of Memory*. Middle: Rachel Song, *Artificial Dream Museum of Film Noir*. Bottom: Daniel Madeiros, *Celestial Cave, Death Valley*. Overleaf, left: George King, *The Blind Architect;* right: Alice Cadogan, *La Maison a Trois*.

A   B   C   D   E

1

2

3

4

5

MUTASI

Dip/MArch Unit 19

Y4: Adam Draper, Roaya Garvey, Richard Meddings, Dan slavinsky, Isabella Theofanopoulos. Y5: Thomas Cartledge, Liwei Chen, John K Fulton, Xiaowei David Liang, Andrew Paine, Thomas Richardson, James Robertson, Matthew Seaber, Mandi Tong. MArch: Charlotte Erckrath, Tim Norman

Parallel Botany, Parallel Biology and Parallel Architecture

With precision, with authority, with wit, with ineffable brilliance of supreme scholarship, Leo Lionni , in his book "Paralell Botany", presents the first full-scale guide to the world of parallel plants – a vast, ramified, extremely peculiar, and wholly imaginary plant kingdom. It is a botany alive with wonders from Tirillus silvador of the High Andes (whose habit it is to emit shrill whistles on clear nights in January and February) to the woodland Tweezers (it was a Japanese parallel botanist Uchigaki who first noticed the unsettling relationship between the growth pattern of a group of Tweezers and a winning layout of Go) to the Artisia (whose various forms anticipate the work of such artists as Arp and Calder – and some believe, the work of all artists, including those not born).

This year Unit 19 considered Parallel architecture and its bio-engineered linaments. It found suitably complex sites and created great works of Parallelism. These works pushed the boundaries of architecture deep into botany and biology and talk of time-based architectural space, ethics and new technology, ecology, different ways of seeing, ascalarity, epistemology, cyborgian geography and archaeology.

In conclusion there is little that is impossible, florescent rabbits have been bred, stem cells have been wired up to drawing machines (what status has art when its artist was never born?). Stelarc has grown an ear on his arm and many, many more polemic biotechnical art projects have been created. It is now time for architects to address these very important issues and ethics.

Neil Spiller and Phil Watson

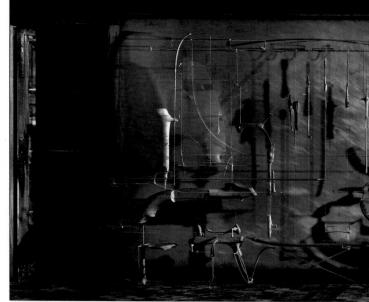

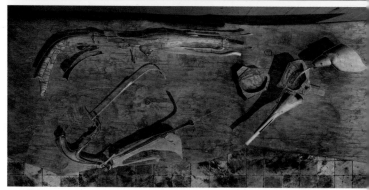

This page and opposite: Tom Cartledge.

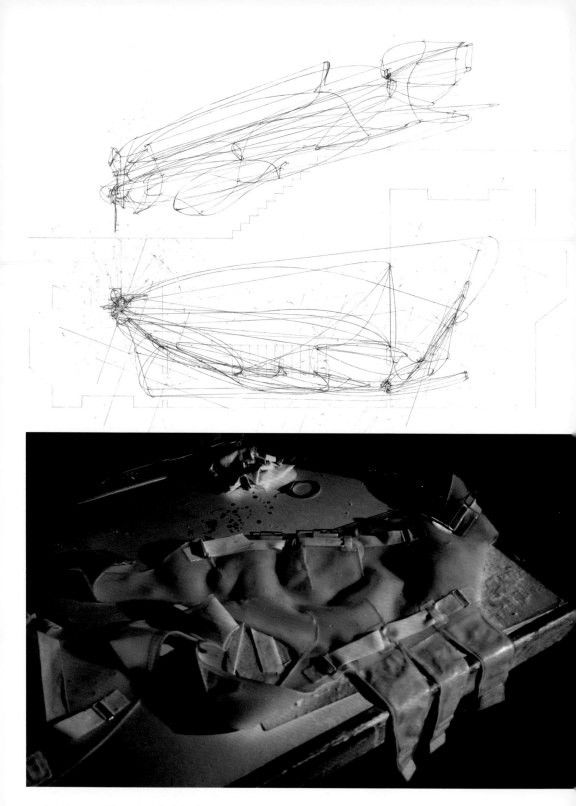

Top: Tim Norman. Bottom: Charlotte Erckrath.

Top: Adam Draper. Bottom: Xiaowei David Liang

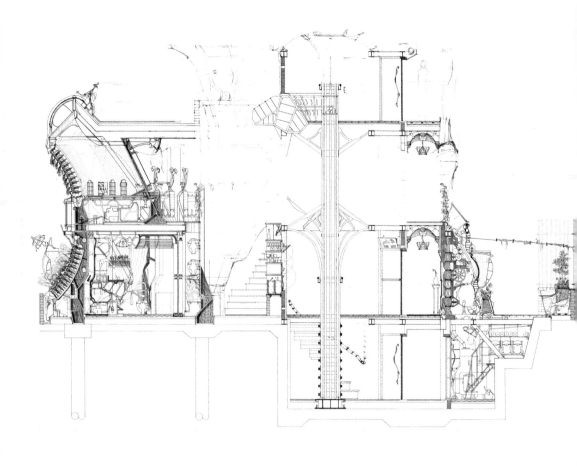

Clockwise from top: Richard Meddings, Liwei Chen, Andrew Paine.

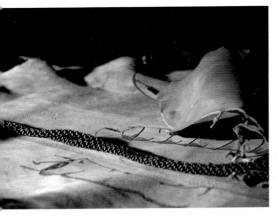

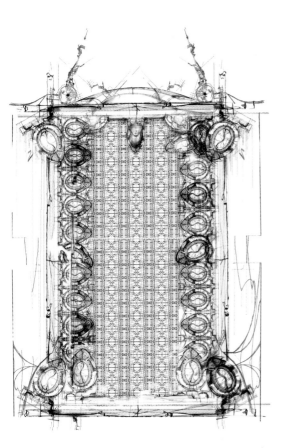

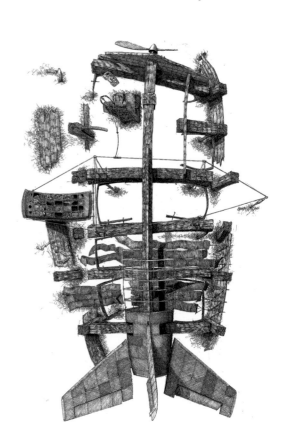

Clockwise from top left:Ronald Cheape, Tom Richardson, James Robertson, Dan Slavinsky.

Dip/MArch Unit 20

Yr 4: Daniel Baumann, Dave Edwards,
Marcin Kurdziel, Hyun Min Koh, Babak Niai
Tizkar. , Brad Sliva, Joanna Szulda.
Yr 5: Jenna Al-Ali, Kasper Ax, Luis Carlos
Reis, Jason Chan, Laurence Dudeney,
Tsehayou Mengistu, Vicky Patsalis, Soraya
Somarthne, Graham Thompson, MArch:
Yousef Al-Mehdari, Johan Voordouw.

Convoluted Flesh

The convoluted (i.e. overlapped,
intertwined and blurred) nature of
contemporary architectural design,
as we understand it, goes beyond the
functions of opulence and intricacy, of
technique and simulation, of module
and optimisation. It invokes something
ranking above notions of beauty, style,
and elegance - it evokes the sublime, the
blissful and the mysterious.

Simultaneously, our understanding of
Flesh in architecture stands in opposition
to the common, yet reductive metaphor
of skin as a flat and thin membrane. In
a time when a lot of the mainstream
architectural discourse is essentially
surface-bound - risking flattening and
disembodying the architectural 'skin' ever
more, the aim of Convoluted Flesh, on the
contrary, is to stress the urgency of a Thick
Embodied Flesh.

Our endeavour is then to establish
a debate in which experimentation,
technology and progress does neither
exclude the intuitive and poetic freedom
of designers as truly creative thinkers, nor
the inherent relationship between the user
and the depth of the architectural flesh.
Hence, we consider a poetic, as well as
'corpological' approach that complement
a typological, topological and ecological
understanding of architecture. At the
same time, we pursue an approach
that develops from inside out, involving
experiential qualities, inhabitation and
use.

Marcos Cruz and Marjan Colletti   This page: Graham Thompson.

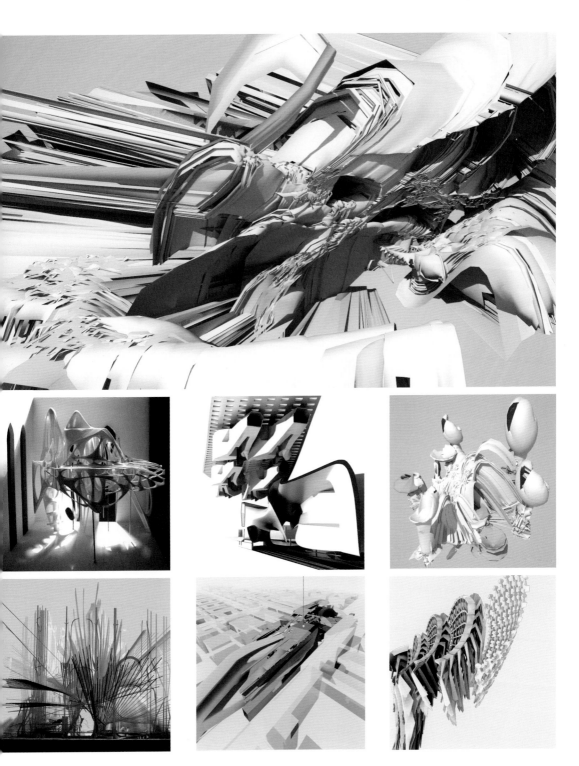

Top: Jenna Al-Ali, Middle left to right: Jason Chan, Luis Carlos Reis, Jenna Al-Ali, Bottom left to right: Tsehayou Mengistu, Luis Carlos Reis, Gareth Evans.

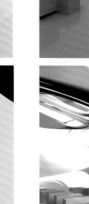

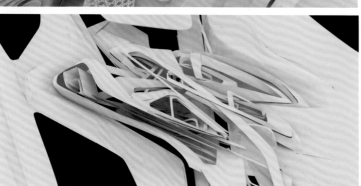

Top and middle: Kasper Ax, Bottom: Laurence Dudeney.

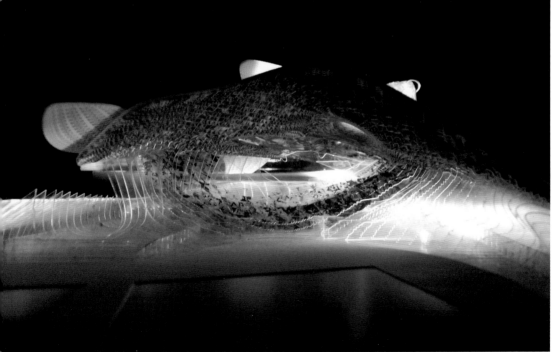

Top: Vicky Patsalis, Bottom: Kasper Ax.

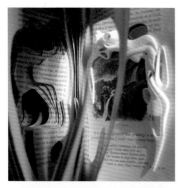

Top: Johan Voordouw, Bottom: Soraya Somarathne.

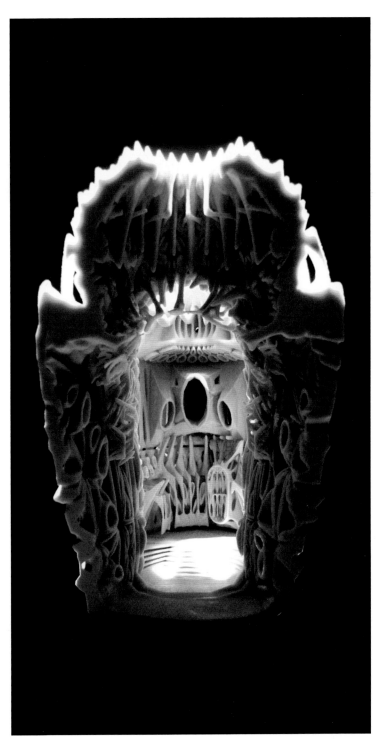

Top left: Jason Chan, Middle left: Jenna Al-Ali, Bottom left: Yousef Al-Mehdari, Right: Yousef Al-Mehdari.

Dip/MArch Unit 21

Yr 4: Zak Keene, Sarah Brighton, Laurence
Mackman, Andrew Walker. Yr 5: Carrie
Behar, Katie Walmsley, William Aitken,
John Lawlor, Bilal Malik, Chein Chin-Yin,
Carolina Razelli, Raphaela Potter

Interchange - *space/ object/ narrative

An intertwining set of themes ran
throughout the programme this year,
it will (in essence) involving reading the
city, interpreting place and constructing
narrative. The project sequence is aware
of, and responsive to, all aspects of
environment.

Three areas of London are offered, each
with a particular character, they have
a life that is both dynamically of the
moment and a hidden history with ghostly
memories of the past. The observer must
paint a picture of this place, a poetic
interpretation of context.

Thanks to Julie Stewart

**Christine Hawley, Abigail Ashton
and Andrew Porter**

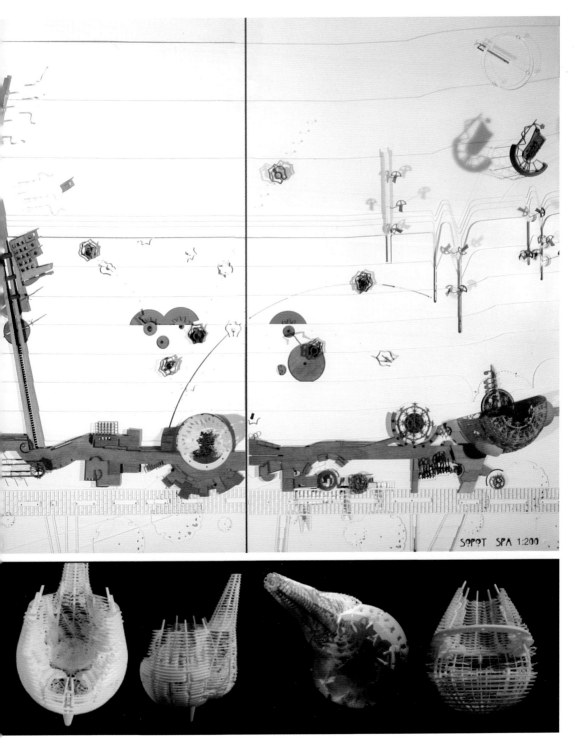

Clockwise from Top: Carrie Behar, *Sopot Beach Spa*; Will Aitken, *Willesden Market and Scout Camp*

Above: Katie Walmsley, *House Theatre*. Opposite Page Top Row: Sarah Brighton, *Anamorphic Pleasure Garden*; John Lawlor, *Productive Landscape*; Zak Keene, *Greenway Follies: The Ghosted Cooling Tower of Abbey Mills Pumping Station*.

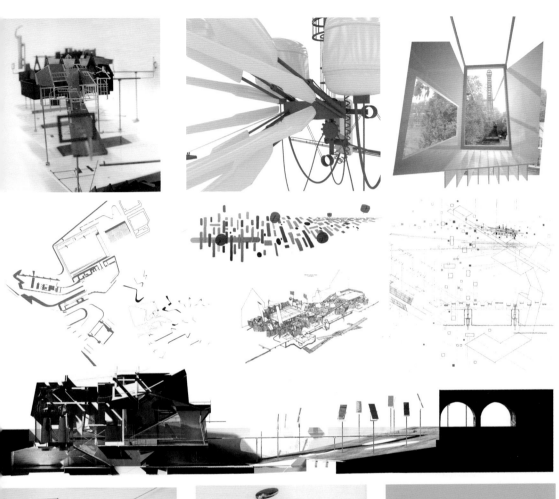

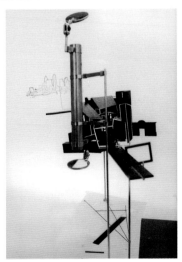

Second Row: Bilal Malik, *Urban Calligraphy*; John Lawlor, *Productive Landscape*; Will Aitken, *Willesden Market and Scout Camp*; Laurence Mackman, *Kinetic Garden*; 3rd Row: Chein Chin-Yin, *Old Kent Road Lido*. Bottom Row: Will Aitken, *Willesden Market and Scout Camp*, Sarah Brighton, *Anamorphic Pleasure Garden*, Zak Keene, *Morphing Tidal Funhouse*.

This Page & Facing Page: Katie Walmsley, *House Theatre*.

1:50 Section Through the Garden Theatre

Dip/MArch Unit 23

Yr 4: Marcus Brett, Chris Campbell, Michael Dean, Sam Frankland, Misha Smith, Alvin Tan, William Trossell, Peter Webb. Yr 5: James Barrington, Francis Gilks, Justin Goodyer, Richard Lipson, Matthew Shaw, Timothy Tasker, Katrina Varian, Andrew Yorke. MArch: Lucy Reuter, Umut Yamac.

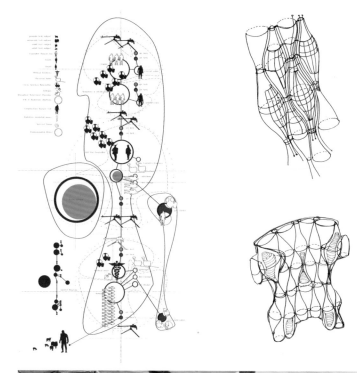

Manufacturing The Bespoke

The unit continues to pioneer and establish innovative and critical positions between analogue and digital design. In 08-09 it continued to transgress disciplinary protocols between the ideal and the real by infiltrating realms of architectural production beyond reach of the desk bound or paper based designer. Our tools are melded with those of the seamstress, the cabinetmaker and their digital siblings. Our knowledge evolves through tacit experience and inquisitive intuition; through the actions of forming, honing, assembly and testing; and with every step, extrapolation and proposition.

This year the unit was propelled by its ongoing investigation into Protoarchitecture through questions of self-sufficiency, interdependency, adaptation synthesis and ephemeralization. In the first half of the year, we surveyed the bombarded hulk of Orford ness in Suffolk, treating it as our laboratory bench upon which to conjure, invent and breed a new species of architectural construct.

In the second sector we formed a convoy through Northern Europe's scarred wasteland, through Zollverin and Dessau, Blankenburg and Wachendorf. We saw 55/02 in incubation and shared suckling pig and Trappist beers with its inspiring craftsmen.

Special thanks to our critics:

Rachel Armstrong, Paul Bavister, Matt Butcher, Marjan Colletti, Kate Davies, Max Dewdney, Murray Fraser, Stephen Gage, Simon Herron, Asif Khan, Tom Lomax, Stuart Munro, Shuan Murray, Ron Packman, Peg Rawes, Matthias Suchart, Neil Spiller, Ben Sweeting, Jerry Tate, Sara Turnbull, Nina Vollenbroker, Michael Wihart, Graeme Williamson and Liam Young.

Bob Sheil and Emmanuel Vercruysse

Clockwise from top: Marcus Brett *'Post Apocalyptic Quarantine Tactics'*, Pete Webb *'Seaside Prosthetics'*, Misha Smith *'Prototype for Acoustic Ecology'*.

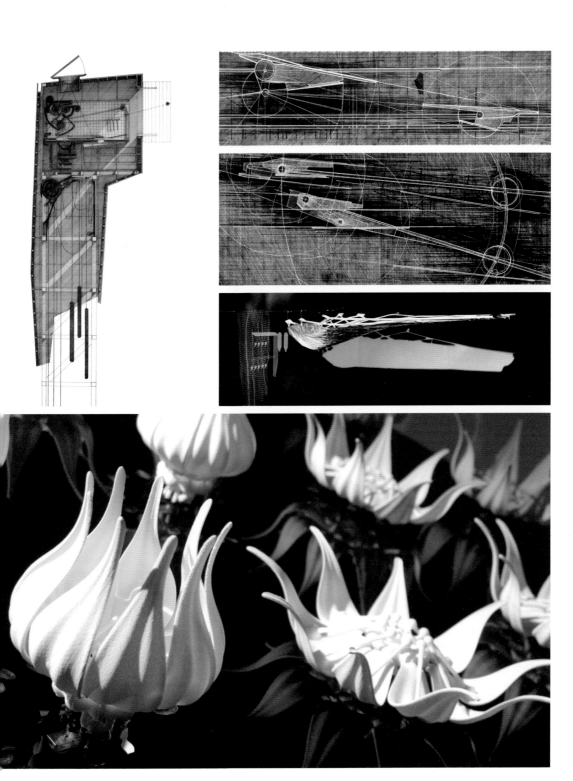

Clockwise from top: Michael Dean *'Outlines of an Ordnance House'*, Will Trossell *'Good, becoming Moderate later'*, Justin Goodyer *'Prototype for Adaptive Bloom'*.

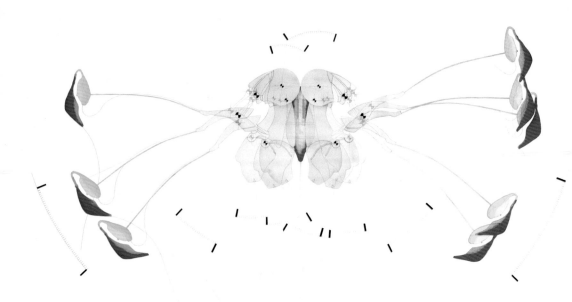

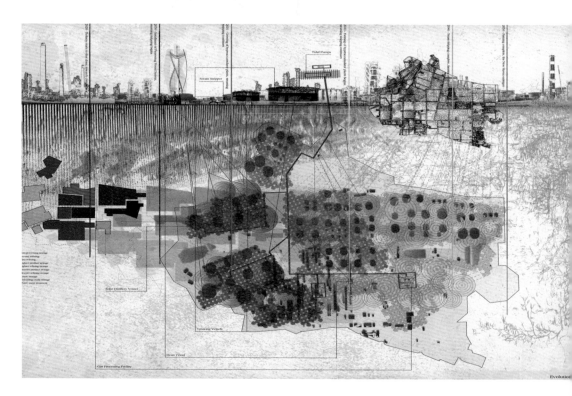

Top: James Barrington: *'Chthonian Ecology: Physiology of a Mechanic Phylum (Charon; The Boatman)* Bottom: Andrew Yorke *'Oil and Soil; The Resurrection of Milford Haven'*

Clockwise from Top: Katerina Varian *'The Tlonian island; an architectural interpretation in relation to the art of memory -The black circle of the indefinite present'*, Tim Tasker *'Cleansing the City' (Section through the FSA as Bathhouse)*. Frank Gilks *'Afterlife of an Island, A Will'o-wisp' drinking/plotting table'*.

Ric Lipson 'Hear, Here' an acoustic theatre modified by inhabitation. Overleaf: Matt Shaw 'Stealth Space; Subverting the LiDAR Landscape in Parliament's Zone of Ambiguity'.

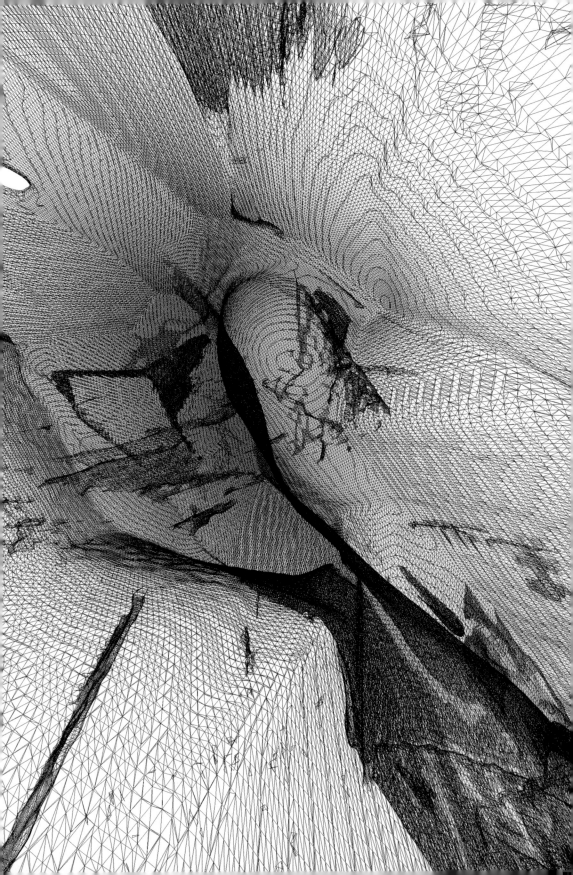

Dip/MArch Unit 24

Y4: Maya Cochrane, Nicole Dixon, Thomas Ibbitson, Kevin Kelly, Tomonori Ogata, Asako Sengoku, Chun-Tai Tsai, Andrea Wong. Y5: Jonathan P Harvey, Christopher Hildrey, Milad Hossainzadeh, Gerald Huber, Bleddyn R Jones, Fei Meng, Thomas J Rigley

Migrating Thresholds

Art protects us from the desert of reality, its one-dimensionality and the complete usefulness and banality of our existence. She achieves that by luring us into new and extraordinary emotional, experiential and intellectual states. In search of original pleasure, architectural designers often endeavour to challenge the unknown but feel restrained by the consequences of the known. We couldn't care less.

There are spaces where duration and memory are compressed. Thresholds can be spatial, chemical, social, etc. They always have potential and they are the sites of change. The term 'threshold' describes moments of transitions. How do we record it? How do we, as architectural designers, imbue thresholds with meaning?

In its first year the unit has zoomed into transitional practices and observed rites of passage and their relevance to our coexistence and in turn invented new passage tactics and rites and responded with articulate architectural observations, experiments and propositions. We have explored thresholds between craftmanship and experimentation; between the excellence of the expectable and the failure of the experiment. We understand thresholds as sites of potential beginning, contact connection, immersion and their antagonists at the same time.

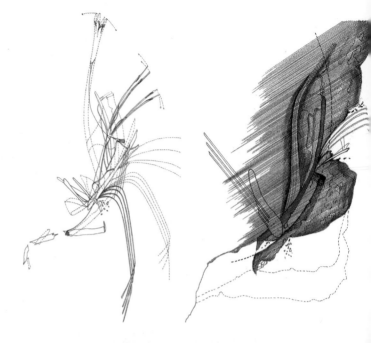

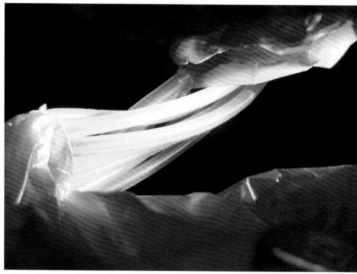

Top: Thomas Ibbitson, *The beginning of architecture in the Garden of Eden*
Bottom: Asako Sengoku, *Inflatable dress.*

Michael Wihart and Uwe Schmidt-Hess

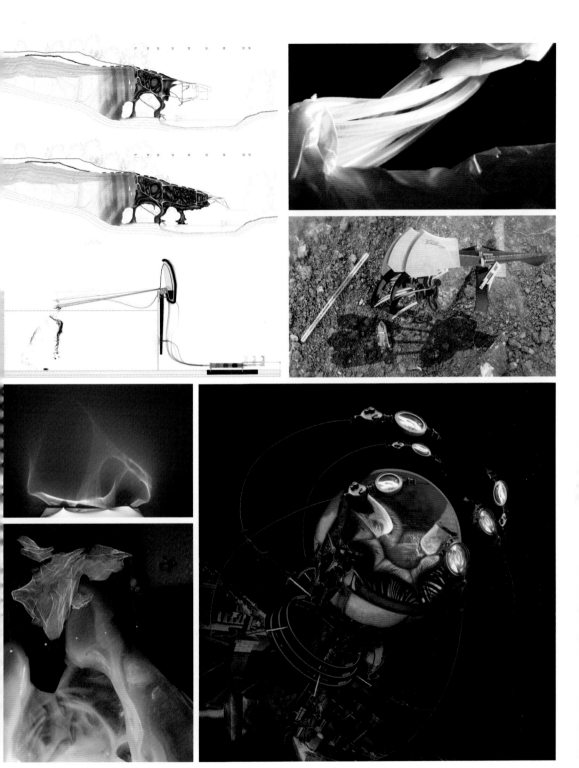

Clockwise from top left: Bleddyn R Jones, *Geo-mechanical bridge at the Dripping Well* in Knaresborough, North Yorkshire; Andrea Wong, *Transfigured anatomies of a shopping bag;* Fei Meng, *Archaeological prosthetics for the Schliemann excavations of Troy,* Turkey; Kevin Kelly, *Lunatic Window;* Chun-Tai Tsai, *Moments of transformation;* Tomonori Ogata, *The visio-computational space of Anatoli Karpov;* Thomas J Rigley, *Aqueous transmission.*

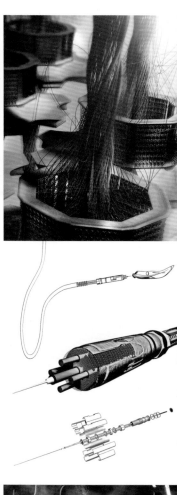
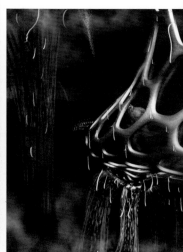

Milad Hossainzadeh, *The Library of Bioinformatics Exchange, Sarajevo.*

Maya Cochrane, *Pores for a Hamam hydraulique*.

Christopher Hildrey, *Hybrid Gardens of the Circle Line, London.*

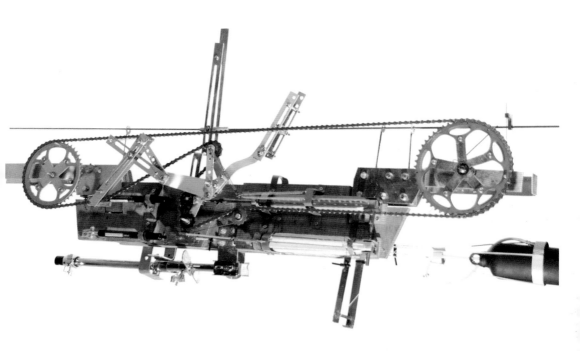

Jonathan P Harvey, *Mistral Festival in Orange, France.*

Dip/MArch Year 5
Thesis

Year 5 Thesis

The thesis is the place where Year 5 students have the opportunity to develop a series of focused research questions that underpin their design work. These questions may be informed by disciplines such as, architectural, scientific, cultural, technological, literary, historical or philosophical theories. As a result, a reflexive relationship is created between the portfolio and thesis, each informing the other.

Peg Rawes, Stephen Gage
Thesis Co-ordinators

Kasper Ax: The Actually Virtual and the Virtually Actual

This thesis investigates the possibility of integrating theories of visual perception into an architectural design practice which employs computer-aided design and computer-aided manufacturing.

Based on architectural representation as the common ground of discussion for the distinct disciplines of CAD/CAM and perception psychology, an exploration into the parallel realms of the actual and the virtual is undertaken. This initiates a narrative that aims to unify matter and manner in digital architecture.

The argumentation proposes an architectural process where tools and ideas, digital and non-digital, continuously complement and contest each other in the endeavour to enrich computer-aided architectural expression.

Lucy Jones: The City on the Back

This document aims to make real a 'non-place': a city fragment to be worn on the back. This fragment operates as a metaphor, which is made explicit by the juxtaposition of the ordinary and the purely imaginary, as well as through the dramatic shift in scale, from the human body to the city itself. The body is used to imply a metaphorical city, representative of the virtual city and particular to the individual, interacting with both the psyche and material experience. The city fragment uses the systems of the body for its needs, and interacts with the body in a physical sense. This duality aims to place my project in a cultural and intellectual context, as well as to serve as a technical exploration.

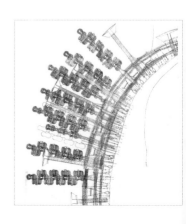

Sam McElhinney: Labyrinths, Mazes and the Spaces Inbetween

The ancient cultural symbol-device of the labyrinth offers archetypes of the architect and of artifice. This thesis contends that a comprehensive examination of the phenomena of labyrinths and their counterpoint, the maze, leads to an understanding that parallels and facilitates the task of constructing the user. A bipolar model is suggested that offers a comment upon themes of spatial perception and cognition: the maze-user employs an external dialogue with the environment, whilst the labyrinth-user internalises the dialogue. The premise is that space is found, experienced and inhabited in a state of 'switching' flux between the typologies of maze and labyrinth.

Michiko Sumi: Constructing Robben Island

The site of my project was Robben Island, Cape Town. In recent years, the island and its significant history have been given a new value as a tourist destination. I predict that this current meaning is unsustainable in the long term and will inevitably collapse. In order to test this hypothesis I explore how the site could be constructed with plurality of representation. This new site recognises the island's multiple histories, the activities of the birds, waves and wind as well as the current inhabitants that are Robben Island. The claim of this thesis is to capture this plurality whilst recognising and embracing the role of my own subjectivity in the construction of representations. I have laid these representations out as 'strata' – a layering that occurs in space and time through the pages of the text.

Richard Bevan: Syn Notation

Digital media allows for design processes in a seamless multisensory environment where sound, form and animation are interdependent. Can a cross-disciplinary 'notation system' help document and provide adequate structure to my own research into timed scaled sound, form and film? The notion is designed on four levels – micro, component, meso, micro – in relation to time to provide a backbone of the entire associative process, and encompasses other core structural relations including: form, frequency, envelope, natural recursion and spatial position.

The notation aims to assimilate a cross-disciplinary language, capable of adaptation and evolution in response to the ever-changing sonic and spatial conditions within my research film. I hope it may provide a working example towards Stan Allen's suggestion for a radicalisation of architectural drawing in response to time-based disciplines such as film, music and performance.

Poem2:   *8 by 8 foot*

8 foot by 8 foot:
is the size of a single cell built around a yard,
Makhukukutu in Afrikaans. [92]
The empty courtyard,
known for torture and humiliation
displayed in pictures
sitting on the flat concrete ground.
Walls squaring up the clear sky.

8 foot by 8 foot:
This is the size of 88 single cells
where the leaders of the political prisoners stayed.

8 foot by 8 foot:
This is the size,
the minimum size for human inhabitation on the island. [92]

MArch Architecture

Students 2008-9: Yousef Al-Mehdari,
Michael Aling, Robert Clement, Charlotte
Erckrath, Daniel Farmer, Michael
Kirkwood, Jonathan Nizzi, Tim Norman,
Ruth Oldman, Harry Parr, Umit Yamac,
Tumpa Yasmine.

In the MArch Architecture degree (non-
Part 2), students produce an original and
sustained investigation focusing on one
of the areas of design, history & theory,
professional studies, technology, or a
combination of these areas. In the area of
professional studies, this work can also be
related to the Certificate in Professional
Practice and Management in Architecture
(ARB/RIBA Part 3).

Tim Norman

**The Cosmic Tea Break: Unique forms of
Tasseography in space.**

The project is about drawing a tea break
as though it were a cosmological event,
beginning with the assumption that the
observer (the one making the tea) is
static within the system, an inertial frame
of reference. Space and objects appear
to orbit an ocular-centric universe. "The
Earth is my eye, I carry the [sp]oon in my
hand outstretched".

Programme Directors: Neil Spiller and Susan Ware

MArch Architectural Design

Students 2007-08: Christina Achtypi, Jana Beermann, Jie Bian, Jie Bian , Mataira Castro Carmen , Carmen Castro , Ko Fen Chen , Hsuan Chen , Achiranon Chungsomboonnanon, Tala Forouzan , Ji Stephen Gan , Cordelia Haenel, Daniel Hedner , Daniel Hedner , Choi Ho , Takayuki Ishii , Husain Jaorawala, Hyun Ju Jeong , Ritesh Joshi, Eleftheria Kapsali, Raza Khan, Kobpong Khomson , Angeliki Koutsandrea, Yi Peng Li, Hongdi Li , Jingxin Li , Alex Limb , Chia Hui Lin, Emma Maria Lindegard Holmstrom , Angeliki Malakasioti, Max Malein , Casey McSweaney , Casey McSweeney, Andrea Panizzo, Dirk Pause , Christos Pylarinos , Xiaohang Iris Qian, Ashok Raveendran , Khan Raza , John Pattrick Rooney , Goetz Schrader , Mansi Shah, Khushboo Sitapara , Nicolas Stearns, Lin Wei Sung, Simon Takasaki, Cheng zhong Tan , Shonan Trehan , Charlotte Tzu-Yuan Tsai, Prateek Vangikar , Pei-An Wei , Chongyin Xu, Ye Yuan

Advanced Virtual And Technological Architecture Research (AVATAR)

The masters studio in architectural design is a 12-month full-time programme concentrating on advanced design. It directly encourages the individual to discover her or his individual expression. The first three months introduce students to the theoretical concepts which underpin AVATAR through lectures and initial design projects. Students then confirm the subject of their thesis project and work in specialist teaching groups. There is continuous discussion of work via tutorials and reviews.

The programme is designed for both recent graduates and for qualified architects: people who wish to be part of a more speculative design environment. In its first decade, the programme has attracted students from more than 35 different countries, many of whom have been awarded major scholarships, bursaries and prizes.

In-house critics include Prof Iain Borden, Prof Colin Fournier, Prof Christine Hawley, Prof Jonathan Hill, Prof cj Lim and many other Bartlett Architecture staff. The masters' studio is also visited by renowned critics: recent visitors have included Thom Mayne, Lebbeus Woods, Elizabeth Diller, Neil Denari and the late Enric Miralles.

Programme Director: Neil Spiller. Tutors: Rachel Armstrong, Nic Clear, Randolph Glanville, Simon Herron, Stuart Munro, Shaun Murray, Andrew Porter, Neil Spiller, Phil Watson

This page: Angeliki Malakasioti

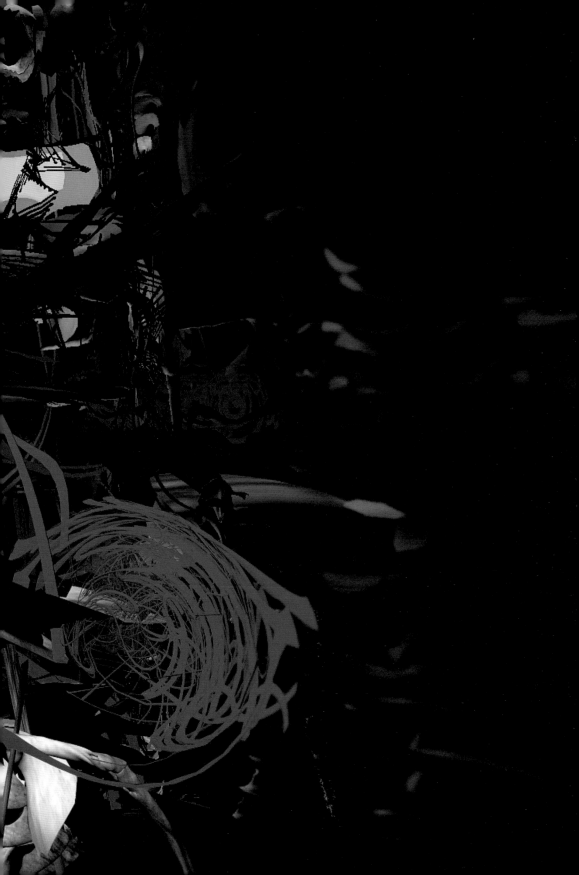

This page: Angeliki Malakasioti

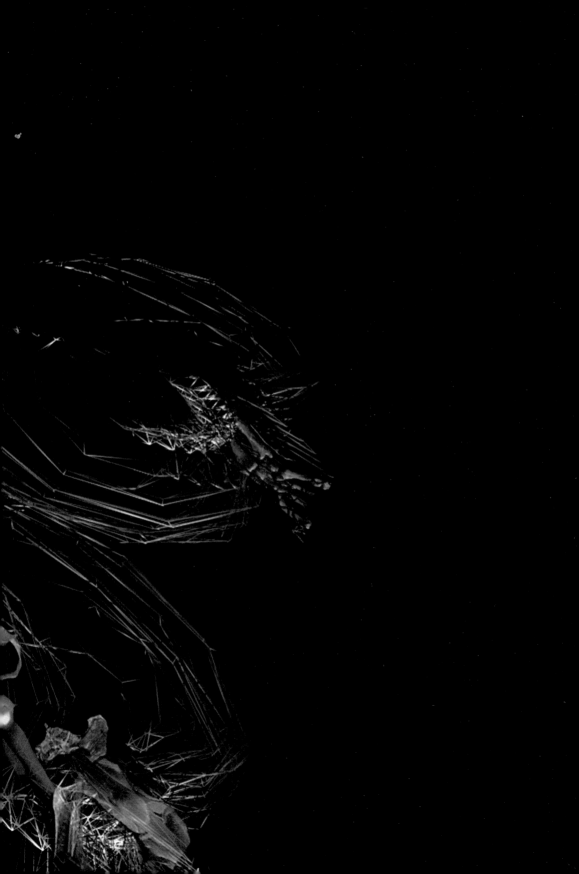

This page: Angeliki Malakasioti

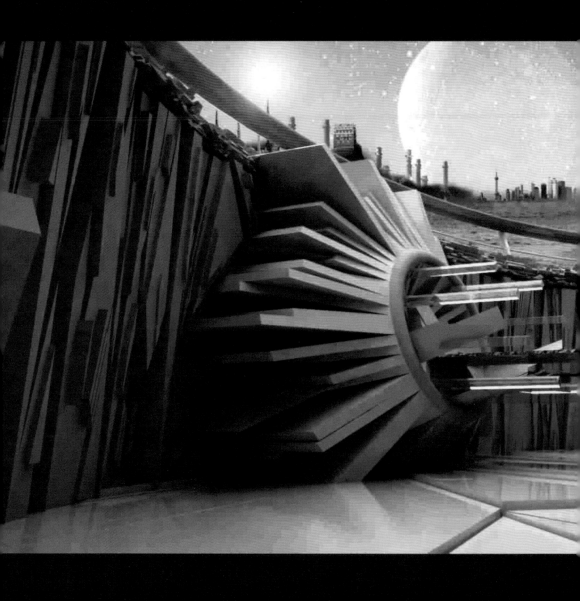

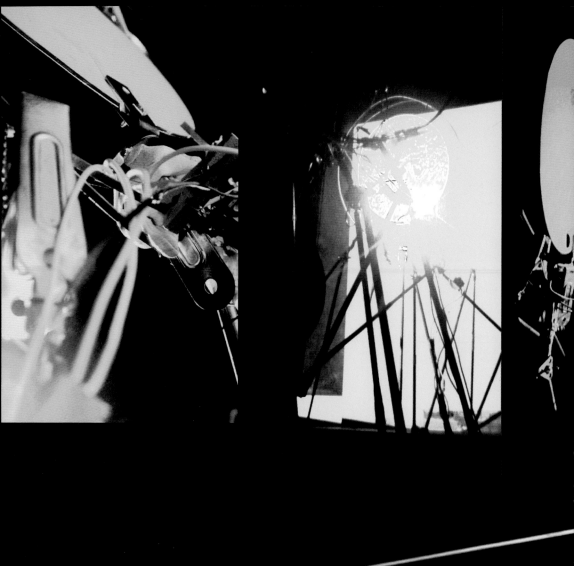

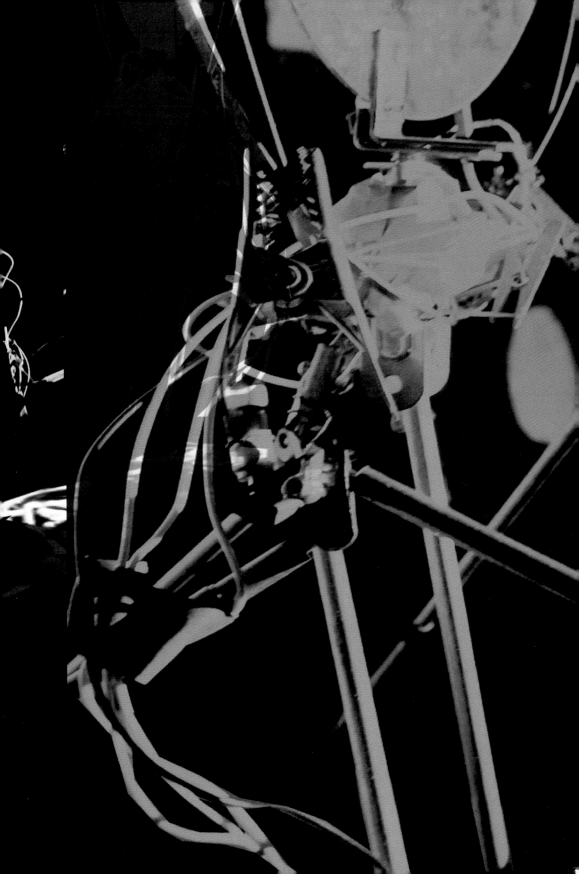

MArch Urban Design

Students 2007-8: Rumi Bose, Mayura Chandekar, Louise Clarke, Barbara Casini, Kostas Dimitrantzos, Lindsay Franta, Marella Anne Fernandes, Chomchon Fusinpaiboon, Xuelan Gong, Paola Guzman, Faye Antonia Hays, Miguel Hincapie, Honghao Ji, Aparna Joshi, Nora Karastergiou, Hyung Koo Kim, Hanki Kim, Ji Hyun Kim, Vipra Kothary, Michelle Kwok, Na Li, Georgia Loizou, Amanda Lwin, Graciela Moreno, Chan Young Park, Tom Pearson, Panayiota Pieri, Niveditha Rajasekeran, Lavinia Rizzo-Haas, Namrata Sharma, Kiavash Soltani, Hiroshi Takeyama, Dominyka Togonidze, Peyman Toosi, Saurabh Vaidya, Vilma Volkovaite, Yang Xiao, Lan Yu.

The course has continued its investigations into urban sustainability. We have maintained an open attitude to interpretations of an issue that has become devalued through overuse.

This year we turned our attention to London. The students started by undertaking group research, initiating a number of investigations of the city in terms of historical growth, geographic and environmental characteristics, urban morphology, relationships between built form and open space, infrastructure systems as well as socio-economic, political and cultural variables.

The students then chose sites for their individual design projects and developed their own programmatic agenda, leading to a particularly diverse set of design proposals, from large-scale development strategies to community-led micro interventions.

While dealing with the pressing environmental issues facing London, in particular the imminent threat of flooding, the work was characterised by wit, invention and the personal idiosyncrasies of the students, playfully stretching and testing the edges of the brief.

Programme Director: Colin Fournier. Tutors: Martin Birgel, Jason Coleman, Robert Dye, Yuri Gerrits, Stina Hokby, Jonathan Kendall, Denise Murray.

ITHACA explores the rise of an informal settlement. There the individual merges with his collective conscience while needs and expectations push towards self-organisation.

When the inert space between illegality and regulation is broken through by crisis, pockets of resistance evolve in their heterotypic dimension. The relationship with power changes irreversibly.

01:00 03:00 crime and punishment

03:00 05:45 development

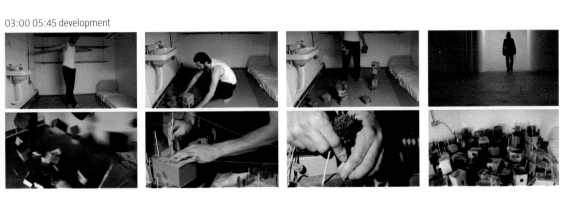

05:45 07:30 memories and resources

Barbara Casini, *Necessity. Mutual Aid. Utopia.*

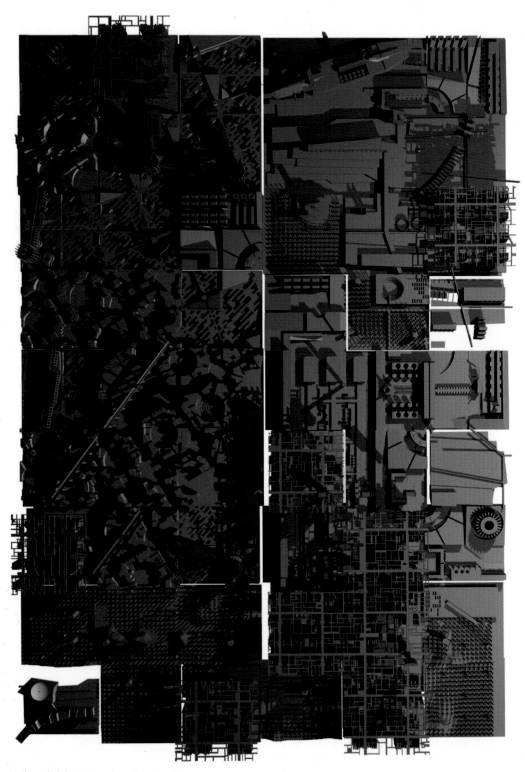

Konstantinos Dimitriantzos and Saurabh Vaidya, *ABBAU+*.

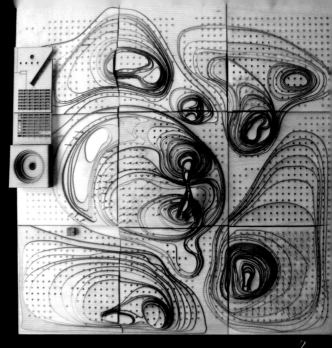

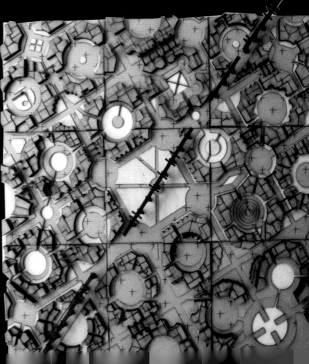

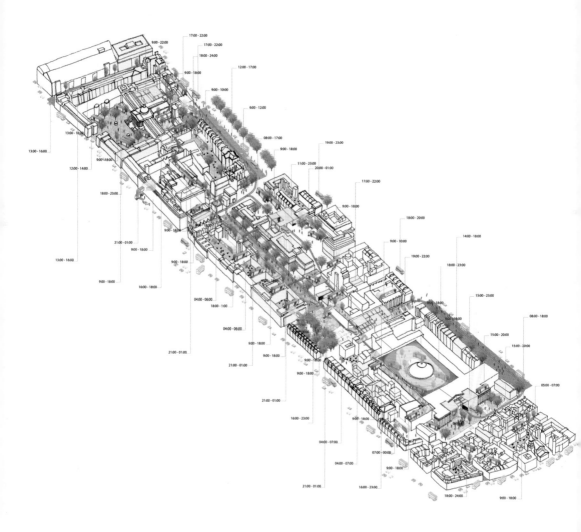

Chomchon Fusinpaiboon, *Ephemeral Bloomsbury.*

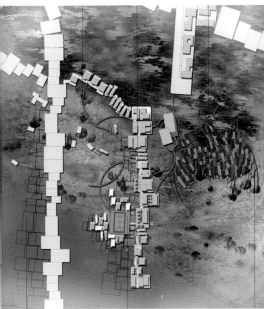

Na Li and Xuelan Gong, *Amphibious City*.

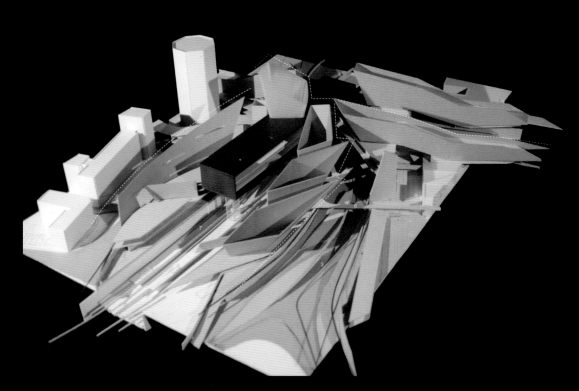

Miguel Hincapie, *Contact Buttons*.

Dominyka Togonidze and Vilma Volkovaite, *Alter City*.

MA/MSc Architectural History

Graduating students 2008: Amber Burrow-Goldhahn, Nadia Carnovale, Ros Croker, Emma Jones, Sandra Kreidel, Torsten Lane, Janna Lipsy, Louis Moreo, Nisreen Moustafa, Piangor Pattayakorn, Gurmeet Sian, Alex Tait, Jason Vir.

Started in 1981, the MA in Architectural History is a unique institution in the field of architectural history, theory and criticism. Over the past 28 years it has provided a coherent and intensive forum in which students develop and test their own approach to the subject, engaging with established and emerging subjects, theories and methodologies. The work produced is innovative and rigorous, and many graduates from the programme have gone on to research, teach and publish at universities and other institutions worldwide.

Organised around a cohesive set of core methodological and inter-related option modules, and lasting for 12 months, the programme is taught by Prof Iain Borden, Ben Campkin, Prof Adrian Forty, (Course Director), Dr Barbara Penner and Prof Jane Rendell.

Over the past twenty-eight years the course has been continually developed and revised, prioritising the exploration of new and existing methodologies and critical theories as they might be applied to the study of architecture and cities. Rather than dealing with architecture solely through the work of famous individuals, stylistic classification or normative categories, the course locates architecture within social, ideological, creative, political and urban processes, and in doing so explores the boundaries of what might be regarded as legitimate architectural objects of study, and of the interpretations which might be made of them.

The main focus of the course is on architecture and cities of the 19th,

20th and 21st centuries, but to provide a perspective on the events and interpretation of this period occasional reference is made to a wider range of historical material. The main teaching mode is the seminar, supplemented by lectures from internal staff and visitors, building and gallery visits, video and film screenings, group working and one-to-one tutorials. The Architectural History & Theory section of the Bartlett also organises public lectures by distinguished visiting speakers, focusing on the intersection of historical and critical theory with different kinds of architectural practice, as well as a PhD seminars and conferences on advanced architectural historical, theoretical and critical method.

The course is for architects already qualified or are in the process of qualification, and for graduates of other disciplines such as art history, history, geography or anthropology who wish to develop a specialist knowledge of architectural history or acquire a foundation for research in the history of architecture. The student cohort comprises home, EU and overseas participants. The MA Architectural History provides skills in the historical and critical techniques for the research and critique of any architectural subject. A student having completed the course will be equipped to undertake research in the history, theory or criticism of architecture, and to evaluate work done in that field.

The culmination of the course is a supervised research project undertaken on a topic of the student's choice, the outcome of which is a 10,000 word Report. Excerpts are printed here from two reports which achieved distinctions in 2007-8.

Emma Jones

The Ladies' Gallery: life and death of a gendered space in the House of Commons

My report will consider female presence in spaces that relate to state authority in London from 1835 – 1918. Marking the lifespan of the Ladies' Gallery in the House of Commons, these dates also coincide with significant reforms in the franchise and the militant phase of the women's suffrage campaign.

[...]

The spatial foci of this research are the House of Common's interior, particularly the Chamber, and the public spaces in Westminster that were appropriated during the women's suffrage campaign from 1906 - 1909.

[...]

To posit a gendered reading of the Ladies' Gallery, I am employing a theoretical framework asserting the socially and culturally constructed identity of the sexed body as clarified by Joan Wallach Scott. 1 The term gender necessarily implies the culturally produced ideas about differently sexed bodies and behaviours, which are intrinsically bound up with class-based value systems, during the Victorian and Edwardian periods. As Leonore Davidoff and Catherine Hall have asserted in their study of English Middle-Class society's building patterns from 1750–1850, the female user group of 'women' has been submerged by patriarchal historiography, which has privileged the visibility of the category of 'lady' in its narratives.

My methodology will involve examining representations of female presence in documentation about the building's design and use contained in the Parliamentary Archives. This process

Programme Director: Adrian Forty. Tutors: Iain Borden, Ben Campkin, Adrian Forty, Barbara Penner, Peg Rawes, Jane Rendell

has involved both an act of recovery of information concerning the existence of a space (about which scant knowledge exists prior to its contestation during the suffrage campaign) and an interpretation of the patriarchal authoring of that evidence. Through this archival material, my aim is to illuminate successive ideologies underpinning the production and reproduction of the Ladies' Gallery and to establish its importance as a former element of the House of Common's. During my navigation of the Parliamentary Archives, I have sought to trace the authoring of the space of the Ladies' Gallery and its environs over time.

Although there is an architectural collection for the Houses of Parliament contained within the archive, the interpretative emphasis is on objects as opposed to the consideration of the social and ideological factors shaping both design and human experience of the buildings' spaces. Pinning down the archival whereabouts of the relatively minor details (in scale and possibly therefore perceived importance) of the peripheral interior of the House of Commons is a slippery process. The Houses of Parliament scream monumentality.

[...]

In the House of Commons the central focus is naturally the Chamber where parliamentary debates take place, with opposition parties checking on Government. The images we often see reproduced of Parliament in progress are only of this centre. I propose switching our attention instead to Parliament's audiences. The Ladies' Gallery was one of several viewing areas in the arena surrounding the main chamber, each containing specific groupings of 'strangers' such as in the Reporters' or Speaker's Galleries.2 Media presence during parliamentary debates was only permitted from 1803, which is important to note in the definition of public spheres and distinctions from the state which I will go on to discuss. 3 For journalists in this arena, there is an obvious reason for their presence but the purpose of the other galleries is more ambiguous. What was

the function of a Ladies' Gallery? Given ladies' limited access to participation in political decision-making processes, the primary reason was likely to be for wives of Members of Parliament, or those with similarly familial, or personal, social connections.

[...]

By selecting a marginal space bordering the state proper, I hope to question the way this centre-stage can be reconsidered as containing its own margins, therefore unsettling the narratives preserved by history's own patriarchal structures. Examining the Ladies' Gallery as part of women's public sphere during this period, this paper will look at the experience of this space from a range of vantage points. The veiled architecture of the gallery's construction; its orchestration of a range of gazes, and internal spatial dynamics, provide a critical lens with which to scrutinise gender politics in a time of unprecedented change for women in British history.

[...]

In his history of the building, Maurice Hastings mentions that in 1822 ladies could peek into the House of Commons from a ventilation space above the space's main chandelier.4 At that time there was no space specifically designed for female viewers within the Chamber. During consultations concerning Charles Barry's recreation of the Houses of Parliament, a Select Committee met in 1835 to consider the Admission of Ladies to the Strangers' Gallery.5 At this point there were two buildings in question: the temporary Chamber the architect Robert Smirke was to design whilst Barry's building was in progress, and the permanent House.6

The short proceedings involved evidence being contributed from one journalist with experience of being in the previous Strangers' Gallery and from Smirke who presented and discussed his proposed design solution. Following the precedent of a segregated area for ladies in the House of Lords, cited by Smirke, it was decided that a partitioned space was to be installed as a compartment of the Strangers' Gallery. The implication was

that the space should be for Members of Parliament to be able to admit ladies connected with them, under their names (suggesting their wives or daughters).

The design specification they arrived at for the temporary Ladies' Gallery goes as follows:

That a portion of the Strangers' Gallery at the North end of the House, not exceeding a quarter of the whole, and capable of containing 24 ladies, be set apart for their accommodation, divided by a partition from the rest of the Gallery, and screened in front by an open trellis work. 7

The extraordinary element of their resolution was the invention of a screen, an idea which seems to be casually tacked on to the end of their statement concerning the temporary gallery and not qualified by any aesthetic reasoning. For the permanent House of Commons, Charles Barry was charged with creating a space capable of accommodating up to forty females.8 The idea of the screen was retained in his Chamber. This detail established the gallery as a highly symbolic gilded cage, embedding Victorian ideas of the separate spheres in this unique House.

Although there is no evidence in the committee's report of the rationale informing the notion of the screen, it connotes neo-Gothic architectural conventions such as monastic cloisters. The spatial veiling suggested by what they call the trellis also echoes representations of the harem in Romantic literature, popular in the early nineteenth century.9 This material construct would interrupt its subjects' views transforming them into more self-conscious, sliced up glimpses. This effect of contradictions between transparency and obscurity does not permit full possession of the whole view.

Barry's chamber positioned the Ladies' Gallery on a second storey elevation, above the Reporter's Gallery and outside the chamber proper. The spatial dynamics of this further layering of boundaries removed the sense of privilege that can be associated with the exclusivity of a theatre box. Most significantly, the placement of the Ladies' Gallery in the overall permanent arrangement distanced its subjects from the public sphere of the debates themselves. Millicent Garrett Fawcett, leader of the National Union of Women's Suffrage Societies, described her experience of trying to see the action below:

One great discomfort of the grille was that the interstices of the heavy brass work were not large enough to allow the victims who sat behind it to focus, so that both eyes looked through the same hole. It was like using a gigantic pair of spectacles which did not fit, and made the Ladies' Gallery a grand place for getting headaches.10

Amber Burrow-Goldhahn

Investigating the Spaces of Chernobyl: A Myth of Emptiness and Fullness

At 01:23 on 26 April 1986 a powerful steam explosion destroyed the RBMK reactor in unit 4 of the Chernobyl nuclear power plant in the Polissa region of Ukraine, then part of the Soviet Union. The accident was caused by "gross breaches of the operating procedures by staff and technical inadequacies in the safety systems."11 The subsequent raging fire, which burned for 10 days,12 ruined much of the building and resulted in a vast release of radioactive debris and radionuclides into the atmosphere.

Facts and Myths

A widespread belief is that thousands, if not millions, of people died as a result of the nuclear accident at Chernobyl. However, according to the World Health Organisation (2005) fewer than 50 deaths are directly attributable to radiation exposure as a result of the disaster. Although cases of thyroid cancer have risen among exposed populations (particularly in children and adolescents) the chances of survival are around 99% and there is no significant evidence to suggest a decrease in fertility rates or an increase in congenital malformations as a result of radiation exposure (WHO, 2005). According to a recent Chernobyl Forum13 report "most emergency workers and people living in contaminated areas received relatively low whole body radiation doses comparable to background levels."14 In fact, the scientific community has concurred that detrimental social and psychological effects of the disaster pose a far greater threat to the health and well being of individuals and local communities than that of radiation exposure.15

As a result of official Soviet secrecy and the proliferation of misinformation, which have long enshrouded the event, there is an extensive lack of factual knowledge about the Chernobyl disaster. This clouding of information and abundance of misperceptions has resulted in the disaster accruing a mythic status, locally as well as globally. In affected areas " 'paralyzing fatalism' "16 of an inescapable danger and 'radiophobia' have been widely reported and "people made up their own stories and myths"17 in order to come to terms with and comprehend the events that engulfed them. Further afield, "the very word 'Chernobyl' has become a synonym for 'horrific disaster' "18: 'Chernobyl' has been dubbed 'the worst nuclear accident in human history' and conjures up terrible imagery of uncountable deaths, genetic disease and appalling mutations. In the aftermath the Western media ran all sorts of scare stories, the Times and the BBC, for example, stating "that 30,000 and more people have died in Europe and Russia as a result of exposure to radiation from Chernobyl accident."19 There has been and continues to persist a vast fissure, in local and international discourse, between the 'facts' and the 'myths' surrounding the disaster.

It is in this gap, this space, between fact and story-telling that my own research project is situated: I will take cold facts and constructed myths (ideas and representations) to try and offer a novel insight into a history that continues to haunt the popular Western consciousness, Chernobyl is the embodiment of our fears of nuclear power gone wrong. I will hereby inevitably end up producing my own myth, my own construction, of Chernobyl.

Method and Perspective

The journey that led me to think and write about Chernobyl began with an abstract question: is there such a thing as an empty space? 20 This broad, philosophical starting point inspired further questioning and apparently infinite lines of possible enquiry within the field of architectural history. In attempting to ground my metaphysical questioning in real space and time my mind persistently kept on returning to an example of a space that is quite literally empty. The 'exclusion zone' surrounding the Chernobyl nuclear power plant (NPP) is an evacuated space, a vast tract of land that was emptied of its human contents as a result of dangerous contamination levels after the accident. This empty space, once full with human life and activity, haunted my imagination, establishing itself as a persistent image in my mind. I was drawn to this subject by a peculiar kind of compulsion.

Reading up about Chernobyl I discovered that the exclusion zone (CEZ) has never actually been completely empty (of people). Hundreds of elderly residents, for example, have semi-legally returned to the abandoned villages, reoccupying their cottages and growing their own (radioactive) food. Around 2,500 people pass through the town of Chernobyl on a daily basis, a place that houses the CEZ's administration, whilst the NPP is still manned by a workforce of around 4,000. However, the 'myth' of bleak emptiness continues to be presented and re-presented, evoked, in turn, by the various linguistic labels attributed to the space: 'dead zone', 'zone of alienation', 'forbidden zone', or simply 'the zone'.

I will discuss Chernobyl in spatial terms: I am interested in the empty as well as the not-so empty spaces. Underpinning and weaving its way through my report will be a fundamental dialectic of spatial fullness and emptiness, of what is present and what is absent, of the material and the immaterial. Using this framework of opposition my discussion will span the zone of exclusion and intangible radiation, absent human life and ecological fullness, the abandoned city and the monstrous Sarcophagus. There is no single argument, instead my thesis is an exploration of ideas through spaces and vice-versa an exploration of spaces through ideas.

Due to practical constraints I was unable to visit the spaces under investigation. This distance (the space being empty of myself) is a challenge to be negotiated: how can I know and interpret what is phenomenally unknown to me? I will necessarily be relying on mediated evidence, on representations of the unvisited spaces. My perspective is that of an outsider, looking at representations that are available to me in the UK: I will draw on a range of English-language academic and biographical texts, diagrams, film footage, online sources, maps, photographs and poetry. I will say as much about the actual spaces as the representations I come to understand them through... how are the spaces of interest interpreted and communicated through different media? What layers are added, what myths constructed in the process of mediation? My method will thus offer insights as to how the spaces of Chernobyl have been and continue to be represented to an outside, Western European audience: how they are perceived, interpreted, communicated and received?

MPhil/PhD Architectural Design

Graduating students: Ana Paola Araujo, Chadi Chamoun, Bradley Starkey.

Current students: Adam Adamis, Nadia Amoroso, Lena Stina Andersson, Katherine Bash, Joanne Bristol, Nat Chard, Emma Cheatle, Ines Dantas Ribeiro Bernardes, Catja De Haas, Pablo Gil, Sophie Handler, Teresa Hoskyns, Popi Iacovou, Christiana Ioannou, Jan Kattein, Rosalie Kim, Tae Young Kim, Constance Lau, Kwang Guan Lee, Tea Lim, Ana Luz, Jane Madsen, Igor Marjanovic, Matteo Melioli, Malca Mizrahi, Christos Papastergiou, Kathy O' Donnell, Felix Robbins, Eva Sopeoglou, Ro Spankie, Juliet Sprake, Theo Spyropoulos, Ben Sweeting, Karen Richmond, William Tozer, Neil Wenman, Stefan White, Michael Wihart, Alex Zambelli.

Leading to a PhD in Architecture, the MPhil/PhD Architectural Design allows especially able and reflective designers to undertake research within the Bartlett School of Architecture's speculative and experimental ethos. The first to be established in the UK, the Bartlett MPhil/PhD Architectural Design is internationally recognized as one of the most influential doctoral programmes dedicated to architectural design.

The programme draws on the strengths of design teaching and doctoral research at the Bartlett, encouraging the development of architectural research through the interaction of designing and writing. An architectural design doctoral thesis has two inter-related elements of equal importance—a project and a text—that share a research theme and a productive relationship. The project may be drawn, filmed, modelled, built, or use whatever media is appropriate.

UCL's multi-disciplinary environment offers a stimulating and varied research culture that connects research by architectural design to developments in other disciplines, such as medicine, art, anthropology and digital media. The programme is intended for graduates of architecture and other disciplines, such as art, who wish to pursue research by architectural design. 40 students from over 15 countries are currently enrolled on the programme.

The Bartlett School of Architecture's two PhD programmes organize three annual events for doctoral students. In Term 1, the Bartlett and the UCL Slade School of Fine Art host Research Spaces, a conference and exhibition with speakers from the UK and overseas. This is followed by Research Projects in Term 2, an exhibition and conference with presentations by current practice-based PhD students in UCL. Invited external critics in 2009 were Professor Steven Connor (Birkbeck, University of London), Professor Penny Florence (UCL Slade School of Fine Art), Professor Murray Fraser (University of Westminster) and Dr Felipe Hernandez (University of Liverpool). Throughout the year, Research Conversations seminars are an opportunity for PhD candidates to present work in progress. In addition, students are invited to participate in the Architecture & Interdisciplinary Seminars in the Bartlett and The Creative Thesis in the Slade School of Fine Art, which is tailored to practice-led research.

In December 2008 the 'RIBA President's Award for Research - Outstanding PhD Thesis' was awarded to Marcos Cruz for his thesis, 'The Inhabitable Flesh of Architecture'. Marcos' supervisors were Professor Sir Peter Cook and Professor Jonathan Hill.

Ana Paola Araujo

Patterning: envisioning strategies for thinking and fabricating architecture through the textile-inspired procedures of repeating, masking and scaling

This thesis constitutes an architectural exploration of the theme of pattern. Retrieving a theory formulated in the mid nineteenth century by the German architect Gottfried Semper, it proposes that spatial design might be derived from pattern making. Semper understood architecture as a technique derived from the pattern-based processes of pottery, carpentry, masonry and, mainly, weaving. Countering the tradition predominant in Western culture since the Renaissance, he claimed that architecture belonged to the domain of the crafts, and not, as established by that tradition, to the realm of the visual arts.

The research takes Semper's theory as a starting point, proposing to investigate how his ideas might engender alternative forms of design thinking and making. The thesis' main themes derive from processes of pattern fabrication, focusing especially on textiles and on how they might be thought in relation to architectural production. The first theme, 'Repeating', entwines the rhythmic routines of textile manufacturing with the creation of domesticity, claiming them to be foundational in the cultural construction of architecture. The second theme, 'Masking', analyzes the social roles assigned to pattern in modern Western culture, finding such roles to work inconspicuously in the maintenance of a system of cultural manipulation. The third theme, 'Scaling', compares processes of representation in architecture with ones engaged in pattern design, investigating how they might influence one another, critically and productively.

Programme Director: Jonathan Hill. **Programme Co-ordinator:** Yeoryia Manolopoulou. **Supervisors:** Iain Borden, Victor Buchli, Marjan Colletti, Peter Cook, Marcos Cruz, Penny Florence, Stephen Gage, Ranulph Glanville, Penelope Haralambidou, Christine Hawley, Jonathan Hill, Yeoryia Manolopoulou, Sharon Morris, Barbara Penner, Peg Rawes, Jane Rendell, Neil Spiller, Philip Steadman, Philip Tabor.

The thesis is developed in two parallel but interdependent modes of discourse. The first of them is predominantly text-based. It is located mainly in the late nineteenth century, in a twofold attempt to understand the historical conditions that propitiated the formulation of Semper's ideas and the ones that prevented them from having a further-reaching impact in Western culture. The second discourse is mostly design-based. It engages pattern procedures in design production investigating ways in which they might affect present and future architectural practice.

Jan Kattein

The Architecture Chronicle—Diary of an Architectural Practice

Most books on architecture start when a building is complete, carefully editing out any evidence of the design and production process. As a result, architecture is often seen as a product rather than a process. *The Architecture Chronicle* is about architecture as a practice. It has two parts. The book *Blur: The Making of Nothing*, 2002, by Diller and Scofidio has informed the format of part one. The *Blur* book reports on the design and construction process of the Blur building. Part one is a diary reporting on the realisation of five stage sets and one urban intervention realised between 16 December 2003 and 3 February 2006. The diary is intercepted by references that are carefully integrated in the overall text. The book *Delirious New York: A Retroactive Manifesto for Manhattan*, 1978, by Rem Koolhaas tells the story of the building of New York where the author takes on the role of a 'ghost-writer', putting into perspective the 'mountains of evidence' to discover patterns and strategies. Part two is such a 'retroactive manifesto', mining the projects in the diary for strategies that re-appear throughout, and fortify, *The Architecture Chronicle*.

In his book *Words and Buildings: A Vocabulary of Modern Architecture*, 2000, Adrian Forty observes that the pre-Renaissance architect worked on the building site amongst other tradesmen in an environment of dispersed authorship. It was his ability to draw and to write — acquired during the Italian Renaissance — that allowed the architect to remove himself from the site of construction and to upgrade his status from anonymous craftsman amongst others to artistic creator. Today, new procurement methods have changed the role of the architect in construction projects. To minimise liability, and because of increased specialisation of building professionals, contemporary buildings are designed by a design team. Today, the architect operates once again in an environment of dispersed authorship alongside other design professionals. Visualisers, engineers and sub-contractors also produce drawings while text is written by surveyors or specifiers.

To maintain his status as artistic creator, the architect in *The Architecture Chronicle* takes on three distinct characters. The architect-arbitrator engages the audience

Images. Previous page: Ana Paola Araujo, *Silhouette Dining Box, peephole views*. Above: Jan Kattein, *Luminaire No 1, powered by methane gas*.

to realise the ambitious project. The architect-inventor challenges conventions and questions the social status quo. The architect-activist transgresses the boundary of the profession and enters the construction process. The Architecture Chronicle concludes that the contemporary architect still draws and writes, but it is often the architect's ability to engage and direct that asserts his or her status. To assert his or her status in the design team, the architect's ability to talk and to act is more important than his or her ability to draw and write.

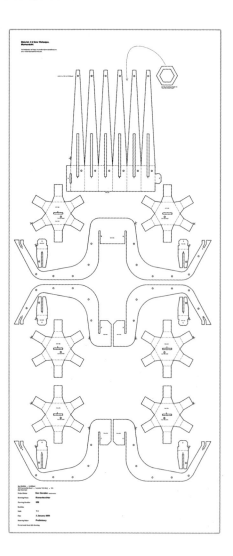

Bradley Starkey

Post-Secular Architecture: The Spiritual in Models of Thought and Models of Architecture

My PhD thesis discusses models of thought and models of architecture with the intention of researching the post-secular. Implying a distinction between pre-secular, secular and post-secular models of thought and suggesting a new openness towards the spiritual, the term post-secular has emerged in various disciplines in recent years. In contrast to some pre-secular models of thought where human beings and the world were believed to be composed of both matter and spirit, dominant models of thought in contemporary Western discourse tend to affirm a materialistic metaphysics, which rejects the whole idea of the spiritual. Crucially post-secular does not imply a regression to the pre-secular since the beneficial achievements of secular thinking are also recognised. Consequently one of the intentions of post-secular thinking is to integrate aspects of the secular with forgotten or previously rejected aspects of the pre-secular, and this involves a questioning of areas of knowledge that have previously thought to be distinct, dissociated and incompatible.

Principally a theoretical design-led investigation, my PhD thesis developed out of a dialogue between designing, making, thinking, perceiving and writing. More specifically, it involved the making of two architectural models. In contrast to the practices of the medieval master mason, the modern architect has generally elevated the status of intellectual or more precisely theoretical labour, above that of manual labour. Traditionally however, the making of an architectural model has involved manual labour and consequently, within the context of architecture's divided labour, the role and status of the architectural model has been rather indeterminate. The architectural model has not been widely subjected to theoretical discussion and architectural models have only rarely played a primary role in the theorisation or conceptualisation of architecture. However, as well as being distanced from the theoretical, they have also been distanced from the spiritual. The intention of this research is to propose a new type of model for architecture – which means both a new model of thought and a new type of architectural model - which questions the division and dissociation between the material, the intellectual and the spiritual. Instead of divided labour, the design-based work advocates integrated labour.

Levitation is a pivotal theme in the thesis and it augments the discussion in multiple ways. Historically levitation can be associated with the pre-secular belief that the material world contained spirit. The theme of levitation re-emerged in Romantic literature as a critique of Enlightenment rationality and it can be interpreted as nostalgia for a pre-Newtonian epistemology. In relation to the design-led investigations discussed in this thesis however, levitation is not regressively nostalgic but is significant as a critical tactic, as an experiential

phenomenon, and as a metaphor in the architectural model.

Like the models of Vitruvius in antiquity, and of the models of Alberti and Filarete in the Renaissance, which provided architects with a model for how they might think and write about their work, my PhD thesis proposes a new type of model. It is my hope that this new type of model might encourage architects to think, design, write, make and build, in ways that recognize, cultivate, employ and enjoy, the material, the intellectual and the spiritual.

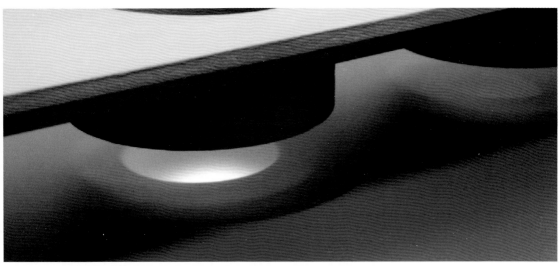

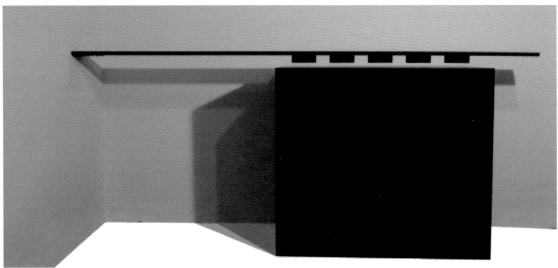

Images. Opposite page: Jan Kattein, Set for Herr Gevatter, *cardboard chandelier template;* This page: Bradley Starkey, *Design Investigation No. 2, detail of levitating plane and up-lit Kiva and side view of base and levitating plane.*

MPhil/PhD Architectural History & Theory

Graduating Student: Aslihan Senel

Current Students: Ricardo Agarez, Tilo Amhoff, Nicholas Beech, Julia Bodenstein, Eva Branscome, Willem de Bruijn, Edward Denison, Alison Hand, Yi-Chih Huang, Anne Hultzsch, Shih-Yao Lai, Tat Lam, Rebecca Litchfield, Yat Ming Loo, Suzanne Macleod, Jacob Paskins, Victoria Perry, Joana Ramalho (affiliate), Sue Robertson, Pinai Sirikiatikul, Lea-Catherine Szacka, Sotirios Varsamis, Nina Vollenbroker

The MPhil/PhD Architectural History & Theory programme allows candidates to conduct an exhaustive piece of research into an area of their own selection and definition. Great importance is placed on the originality of information uncovered, the creativity of the interpretations made, and the rigour of the methodological procedures adopted.

The range of research topics undertaken in the programme is broad, but generally look at the history and theory of architecture and cities from c. 1800 to the present day, with an emphasis on the critical reading of these subjects from cultural, political and experiential viewpoints.

Approximately 20-30 students are enrolled at any one time in this programme. The Bartlett School of Architecture runs an active series of events for students from both the MPhil/PhD Architectural Design programme and the Architectural History and Theory programme to provide a platform for advanced discussions of research methodology. These include a series of departmental seminars (PhD Architecture Research Conversations), an annual student-led conference held in conjunction with the Slade (PhD Architecture Research Spaces), and an annual graduate conference at which students present work to invited respondents (PhD Architecture Research Projects). With the Slade since 2005, we also run a special PhD workshop, The Creative Thesis: Thesis Writing in the Practice Related Arts/Humanities PhD Admission.

Current dissertation titles include:

Julia Bodenstein, The open file —analysing women's' workplace in Britain (1870 –1970)

Edward Denison, Modernism in China - Architectural Visions and Revolutions

Anne Hultzsch, Detaching the Gaze: A Historical Enquiry into the Relation between Looking at and Describing Architecture

Jacob Paskins, The social experience of construction work in and around Paris, 1962-1968

Dr. Aslihan Senel, *"Unfixing Place: A Study of Istanbul through Topographical Practices"*

The aim of this PhD thesis is to redefine topography as a critical practice of space and suggest a method derived from topographical theories and practices for studying architectural and urban history and theory. Identifying traditional and critical topographical theories and practices as fixing and unfixing place respectively, I explore how contemporary urban spaces in Istanbul are produced and reproduced through the topographical practices of twentieth-century tourist maps, city guidebooks, and urban documentary films.

Traditional topographical practices work to orientate users and locate certain knowledge by associating it with certain elements of the city. The mindset behind these kinds of practices assumes stable and single positions of knowledge in relation to place and creates the illusion that topographical practices are neutral representations of reality. But in this research, I propose that topographical practices may also offer new critical ways for thinking traditional topographical methods by reworking their objective and quantitative processes in new subjective and qualitative ways. Critical topographical practices suggest an understanding of topography that is more performative than representational. They use methods such as juxtaposition, superimposition, disorientation, and dislocation in order to shock the viewer

or user and to make them reconsider the established knowledge about a place as well as realize the possibility of multiple and other knowledges of place. I argue that the shift between traditional and critical topographical practices is marked by changing understandings of relationships between place, subject, and representations due to the emergence of poststructuralist and new feminist theories and practices since the 1990s.

Critical topographical practices provide me with tools to question the conventional representations of the city in the architectural and urban history of Istanbul. I explore relationships between conceived and perceived urban spaces in this thesis through both writing and through a critical topographical practice of my own – a digital mapping. This practice addresses fixing and unfixing of place while mapping a viewing of certain documentary films, a reading of certain guidebooks, and a use of certain maps of Istanbul. My practice contains, on the one hand, the mapping of the dominant knowledges of place in the traditional topographical practices I study, and on the other, the unfixing of place in those traditional practices through my partial, fragmentary, and individual mapping, which also brings out the repressed and resistant knowledges in traditional practices. My mapping depends on my own partial and changing knowledge of places in Istanbul in order to relate views, sounds, and texts with each other and the map of the city. As such, my practice resists totality and completeness. This fragmentariness creates gaps between the dominant knowledges of place and allows alternative, multiple and unpredicted knowledges to be formed. The criticality of my topographical practice rises out of the tension between the claimed fixity of place in traditional topographical practices and the display of possibilities of unfixing place. In this way, my practice addresses the co-dependent and changing relationship between fixing and unfixing of place.

My digital mapping is an exploration of the spatiotemporality of documentary films, guidebooks, and maps. It involves operations upon film sequences, texts, sounds, and graphic material that can

Programme Director: Barbara Penner. Supervisors: Jan Birksted, Iain Borden, Adrian Forty, Jonathan Hill, Yeoryia Manolopoulou, Barbara Penner, Peg Rawes, Jane Rendell, Neil Spiller, Philip Steadman, Philip Tabor.

be described as uncovering, cutting, dissecting, and detaching. These operations reveal both the structures of the documentary films, guidebooks, and maps and also the process of making in those. The digital mapping also creates juxtapositions, superimpositions, dislocations, and disorientations with the fragments of films, texts, sounds, and graphics, in order to invite a further interactive engagement with the material, where the user reads, views, interprets, operates, and constructs new meanings in the space between these different fragments. Through these engagements my mapping provides unexpected and changing relationships between different representations of a place. This offers a continuous slippage and dissemination into multiple possibilities of knowledge about that place.

This particular way of working with maps, guidebooks and documentary films of Istanbul has provided me with a critical point of view towards the architectural and urban history of Istanbul, and allowed me to consider in a new way the relationships between contemporary topographical practices and physical and cultural transformations in the city. In this thesis, I argue that topographical practices have been understood as expressions of ideals, such as modernisation, globalisation, and metropolitanisation, throughout the history of the city, and so they affected the way the city is experienced, anticipated and rebuilt.

In the early years of the Republic of Turkey (from 1923 to the 1950s), monuments served to fix a certain understanding of place, the Ottoman history of Istanbul, in order to allow progress and the new constructions of the republic. Maps and guidebooks of the 1930s fixed certain places such as Ottoman Topkapı Palace and Sultanahmet Square as spatial representations of the past – the former as a museum and the latter an archaeological park. At the same time, roads and newly built public spaces such as Taksim Square and Gezi Park were emphasized to represent progress and the new Republic. The ideal urban resident was defined as a citizen actively involved in city life. The maps and guidebooks of

this period encouraged this kind of citizen by offering knowledge of public space and by presenting Istanbul as a combination of a network of roads and monuments. In the 1950s, in parallel to the changes in the spatial organization of the city and the introduction of tourism, guidebooks and maps aimed to produce citizens as tourists. At this time, the number of guidebooks and maps increased, and documentary films also started to be produced.

In the late 1960s and 1970s, Istanbul guidebooks and documentary films fixed Istanbul as composed of certain historical views, which are regarded as the distinct character of the city. To achieve these ideal views, place was fixed as location and as a combination of certain elements. Buildings were regarded as 'belonging' and 'not belonging' to certain places. The panoramic views in the guidebooks and documentary films of the time reflect this understanding by depicting an ideal view and ignoring the modern and the everyday. Some late-1970s documentaries suggested a uniform historical understanding of the city that fix it by focusing on certain historical and more controlled places of the city rather than, for example, squatter areas, which were emerging at the time. This understanding also affected the physical transformation of the city at the time. For example, during certain restorations in the historical centre of Istanbul, certain historical buildings were chosen to represent those places as the authentic Ottoman while some others were demolished. With a similar attitude, certain historical parts, such as facades, of some historical buildings were preserved, while the rest of those buildings were rebuilt.

The critical topographical practices of maps, guidebooks and documentary films of the post-1990s, on the contrary, displace dominant knowledges of place. They juxtapose and superimpose multiple views of the city. In these critical topographical practices, makers and writers adopt more self-reflective roles and expose their methods in order to invite the viewers and readers to participate in their works and the making of place, by questioning the dominant knowledge

and the practices that produce that knowledge. Spatio-temporal juxtaposition and dislocation techniques of these critical topographical practices also reflect a time when multiplicities were acknowledged and civil society became more influential in the urban transformations. In some of the critical topographical practices I studied in this thesis, maps, which are often used as way-finding tools, are dislocated so that they are no longer 'useful', refer to and negate what we know of certain places. The viewing of these works causes disorientation, urging the viewers to question the established knowledge of a place. Similarly, guidebooks are expected to provide content with 'reliable' historical and practical knowledge about a place. Critical topographical practices rely on this kind of expectance and disorientate the readers by offering only subjective, experiential, and unusual knowledge about a place. As such, these works multiply knowledges of a place and show that subjective experiences, memories and dreams play an important part in doing so.

This thesis intends to make an original contribution to the knowledge and understanding of topographical theory and practice in relation to contemporary Istanbul in four ways. First, I use feminist and poststructuralist theories to explore how contemporary maps, guidebooks and documentary films perform rather than represent Istanbul as place – as unfixed, multiple and hybrid. Second, I rethink these often generic theories in relation to the particular topographic practices that map urban space, specifically Istanbul. Third, I critique the conventional understanding of topography as site in architectural theory and recast topography as both site and more importantly practice. Fourth, I propose a critical topographical practice in the form of a digital map, which explores and critiques the maps, guidebooks, and documentary films which are also explored in the text.

This page top: Aslihan Senel, *Tourist's Guide to Istanbul: Map showing how Murat Belge's guidebook, Tourist's Guide to Istanbul (1993), multiplies knowledges of places with subjective experiences, memories and information.* Bottom: Aslihan Senel, *About Istanbul: Mapping the interactions of different experiences in a place in Enis Riza's documentary film, About Istanbul (1990)*

Summer School

The Bartlett School of Architecture will this year host its fourth Summer School. A group of 60 participants ranging in age from 16-50 and from differing backgrounds – including prospective Bartlett students and international students will develop their interest in architecture.

The Bartlett Summer School 2008 was a Micro-festival of Architecture. Students explored the built history of festivals from the South Bank of the Thames to the Crystal Palace looking at the events and their legacy. A design based programme lead to the creation of the elements of the festival. These may be structures, events, films or whatever is required to enliven and excite the spaces around the Bartlett School to attract interested members of the public as well as those in the know.

As part of UCL's Widening Participation Programme we are able to offer 20 sponsored places to secondary school students.

Bartlett Designs

The Bartlett School of Architecture at UCL is one of the world's leading places at which to study and teach architecture. Every year it attracts hundreds of students from around to world to come and participate in its highly experimental and rigorous range of architecture programmes. Its graduates have won an extraordinary range of prizes on the international stage, and are highly sought after by architectural practices globally.

Bartlett Designs: Speculating With Architecture is a collection of the very best of this student work from the last decade. Through a detailed presentation of over 100 student projects, each succinctly explained by the individual tutors concerned, the book shows how architectural designs and ideas can creatively address some of the world's most pressing urban and social problems through buildings and other forms of architectural invention. The wide range of projects on show deal inventively with such important issues as cultural identity, housing, climate change, health and public space, as well as architectural concerns with the imagination of exciting forms and aesthetic languages.

Complementing the student projects is a series of short and provocative essays written by tutors at the school. Ranging from landscape to buildings, from urbanism to interaction, from making to advanced technology, these essays postulate a series of manifestoes and agendas – and so both create a conceptual framework around the incredible variety of student work on display, and suggest some of the most current and pertinent agendas for architecture today.

256 Pages, Full Colour

25.6 x 23.2 x 2.2cm

Published by Wiley, June 2009

Available from the Bartlett and all usual booksellers £20.

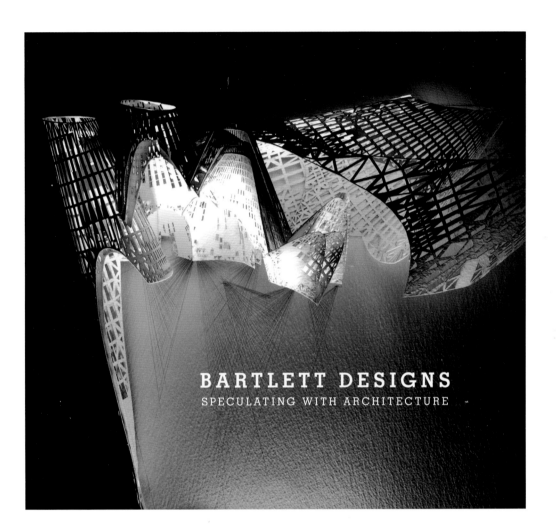

BARTLETT DESIGNS
SPECULATING WITH ARCHITECTURE

Staff

Abi Abdolwahabi, Laura Allen, Kit Allsopp, Tilo Amhoff, Gregor Anderson, Ana Araujo, David Ardill, Rachel Armstrong, Abi Ashton, Martin Avery, Phil Ayres, Julia Backhaus, Katherine Bash, Scott Batty, Nicholas Beech, Johan Berglund, Peter Besle, Elena Besussi, Jan Birksted, Iain Borden, Matthew Bowles, Dan Brady, Thomas Kyle Buchanan, Bim Burton, Michelle Bush, Matthew Butcher, Ben Campkin, Rhys Cannon, Elisabete Cidre, Nic Clear, Jason Coleman, Marjan Colletti, Wendy Colvin, Marcos Cruz, Willem De Bruijn, Max Dewdney, Elizabeth Dow, Robert Dye, Bernd Felsinger, William Firebrace, Pedro Font Alba, J. Adrian Forty, Colin Fournier, Daisy Froud, Stephen Gage, Jean Garrett, Christophe Gerard, Yuri Gerrits Emer Girling, Ranulph Glanville, Richard Grimes, James Hampton, Penelope Haralambidou, Christine Hawley, Simon Herron, Jonathan Hill, Stina Hokby, William Hodgson, Dan Horner, Anne Hultzsch, Susanne Isa, Kevin Jones, Jan Kattein, Jonathan Kendall, Simon Kennedy, Julian Krueger, Stefan Kueppers, Chee-Kit Lai, Lucy Leonard, Saskia Lewis, CJ Lim, Rebecca Litchfield, Katie Lloyd Thomas, Adam Lubinsky, Kim MacNeill, Yeoryia Manolopoulou, Niall McLaughlin, Stoll Michael, Ana Monrabal-Cook, Edouard Moreau, Graciela Mornero Ternero, Stuart Munro, Shaun Murray, Denise Murray, Fabian Neuhaus, Christian Nold, Brian O'Reilly, Nadia O'Hare, Luke Olsen, Barbara Penner, Romed Perfler, Jonathan Pile, Simon Pilling, Frosso Pimenides, Andrew Porter, Hannah Powles, Robert Randall, Peg Rawes, Jane Rendell, Richard Roberts, David Rosenberg, Mark Ruthven, Uwe Schmidt-Hess, Bob Sheil, Naz Siddique, Toby Smith, Paul Smoothy, Mark Smout, Anna Solarska, Neil Spiller, Brian Stater, Gareth Stokes, Wycliffe Stutchbury, Jerry Tate, Ann Thorpe, Michael Tite, Nicholas Travasaros, Emmanuel Vercruysse, Nina Vollenbroker, Susan Ware, Martin Watmough, Phil Watson, Clyde Watson Patrick Weber, Andy Whiting, Michael Wihart, Robin Wilson, Oliver Wilton, Catherine Wood, Matthew Wright, David Yates, Liam Young, Paolo Zaide

The Bartlett School of Architecture would like to thank our sponsors for their generous support

Catalogue

Allford Hall Monaghan Morris

Private Reception

Lee Associates
Deltek

Supporters of the Summer Show

Hamiltons
Metropolitan Workshop
Pringle Brandon
Rogers Stirk Harbour + Partners
Walters and Cohen
White arkitekter

Opener's Prize

White Partners Ltd

Bursaries

Kohn Pedersen Fox Associates
Rogers Stirk Harbour + Partners
The Leverhulme Trust

Bartlett Architecture International Lecture Series

Fletcher Priest Trust

Rogues and Vagabonds

The Rogues and Vagabonds is an alumni group made up of ex-Bartlett students and friends. The group's function is quite simply "to meet, to drink, to eat, and to listen to a good speaker..." This is celebrated through an annual dinner and after-dinner speech given by an invited guest.

For details, T. 020 7679 4642 or email architecture@ucl.ac.uk

Additional Sponsors

The School's programme of publications and associated events has been generously supported by:

Bartlett Architecture Society

UCL Futures

Individual units have also received kind support from numerous other companies and institutions.

Bartlett Architecture Society

Founded in 2000, the Bartlett Architecture Society (BAS) is growing rapidly. Already, the BAS organises a special lecture series and other events. It also contributes to the development of the school through sponsoring equipment purchase, events and publications. Membership is given free to all new graduates to the first academic session after graduation. Annual membership is £40. Open to all former students, staff, and supporters of the Bartlett School of Architecture.

For details, T. 020 7679 4642 or email architecture@ucl.ac.uk

www.fletcherpriest.com

Rogers Stirk Harbour + Partners

Hamiltons

Architects Masterplanners

www.hamiltons-london.com   Hamiltons Prize

KPF

**Kohn Pedersen Fox Associates
(International) PA**
Architects and Planning Consultants

www.kpf.com   Student Bursaries

Metropolitan Workshop

www.metwork.co.uk   Supporter of the Summer Show

PRINGLE BRANDON

www.pringle-brandon.co.uk   Supporter of the Summer Show

Walters and Cohen

white partners.

LEE
ASSOCIATES

accountants to the creative sector

www.leeassociates.co.uk   Private Reception

Deltek

www.deltek.com   Private Reception

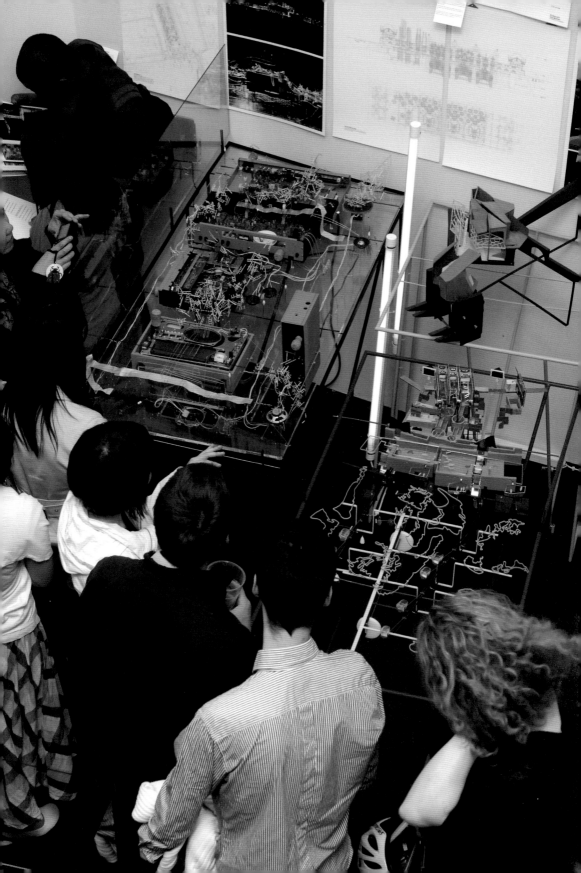

DMC London

London's newest and largest selective laser sintering (SLS) manufacturing bureau now at the Bartlett School of Architecture.

Services include :

SLS Systems

• High resolution, high accuracy models produced in strong durable nylon plastic with ultra white finish

• Material capable of producing bespoke or short run manufactured products/ components

• Production of excellent master models for down stream manufacturing applications

• Form fit function models for pre-production, testing and marketing

Z Corp 3D printers

• Quick and cost effective

• Early design visualisation

• Explore multiple design iterations early

• Models can be used for down stream manufacturing applications

CNC Routing

• 2.5 x 1.5m 3 Axis router table for fabrication of large and medium scale parts

5 Axis milling machine

• Complex parts manufacture

For more information contact Martin Watmough, Director DMC London

Tel: +44 (0)20 7679 8565

Fax: +44 (0)20 7679 5424

Mobile: +44 (0)77 3979 7248

dmc.bartlett@ucl.ac.uk

www.bartlett.ucl.ac.uk/architecture/resources/dmc.htm

Facing page: Graham Thompson, Dip/MArch Unit 20.

Bartlett International Lecture Series

Supported by Fletcher Priest Trust

The Bartlett International Lecture Series features speakers from the Bartlett and across the world.

Forthcoming lectures are publicised within the Bartlett, on the website and through the Bartlett Architecture Listing.

archlist@ucl.ac.uk

www.bartlett.ucl.ac.uk/architecture/events/lectures/lectures

"The Politics of Digital Poetics"

Marjan Colletti

supported by Fletcher Priest Trust

"Recent Projects"

KJETIL THORSEN

supported by Fletcher Priest Trust

"Architectural Studies Open Event"

"L'Architecture Autre - The Other Architecture"

GÜNTHER FEUERSTEIN

supported by Fletcher Priest Trust

"Ummm, Now we're talking"

Hernan Diaz Alonso
Xefirotarch

"Structural Ecologies"

Tom Wiscombe
Principal, EMERGENT

"Le Corbusier and the Occult"

J.K. Birksted
Bartlett School of Architecture, UCL

Book Launch & Bar following Lecture

supported by Fletcher Priest Trust

"Material Computation, Computational Material"

Mette Ramsgard Thomsen
Head of CITA

supported by Fletcher Priest Trust

"Stiloi Guedes and the Bubblics"

Pancho Guedes

supported by Fletcher Priest Trust

"The (Im)Possibility of the Semi-Living"

Oron Catts
SymbioticA-The Centre of Excellence in Biological Arts

supported by Fletcher Priest Trust

"Presumption of Functionality: spatial vandalism"

"The Open City of Amereida"

Mauricio Puentes

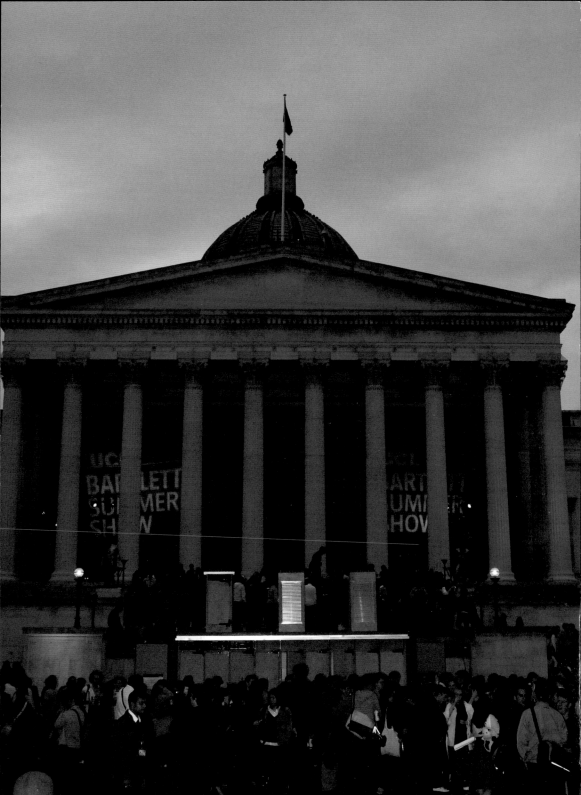

www.bartlett.ucl.ac.uk

Publisher
Bartlett School of Architecture, UCL

Editorial and Design
Iain Borden
Nadia O'Hare, Tom Finch, Luke Pearson

Cover Image
"First Year Installaction", BSc Architecture
First Year, Soane Museum, London.

Printed in England by Quadra Color Ltd

ISBN 978-0-9558331-3-7

For a full range of programmes and
modules please see the *Bartlett
Undergraduate*, *Diploma* & *Graduate
Guides*.

Bartlett School of Architecture, UCL
Wates House, 22 Gordon Street
London WC1H 0QB
T. +44 (0)20 7679 7504
F. +44 (0)20 7679 4831
architecture@ucl.ac.uk
www.bartlett.ucl.ac.uk